'I was told you were a mature woman,' Ellerton snapped.

'Maturity is not necessarily a matter of years,' Anna responded, maddeningly undisturbed by his displeasure. 'I know women in their sixties who act like children.'

And so did he, he thought uncomfortably. 'Are you ill?' he demanded irritably, determined to disconcert her. 'You are as thin as a pole.'

'How uncivil of you to say so,' she said in an amused tone. 'But then, you are notorious for your incivility.'

'And I thought I was notorious for other reasons.'

He had expected this dried-up spinster to blush furiously in speechless embarrassment, but instead she assured him affably, 'Oh, yes, for that, certainly, but for your rudeness as well.'

'What did you say?' he demanded.

To his indignation, instead of answering him immediately, she resumed her careful scrutiny of him from the toes of his well-polished riding boots upward to the unruly black hair that crowned his head. Finally, she responded, 'For a man of your reputation, you are not at all handsome. Nor charming either. I would have thought a man who has had such a parade of celebrated demi-reps under his protection would have had to be both. But then, you are very rich.'

Marlene Suson abandoned a career in journalism after discovering that she preferred historical fiction to contemporary fact. After spending her writing time immersed in the early nineteenth century, she likes to relax with such twentieth-century pursuits as skiing and flying a light plane. She and her husband, who is also a writer and a computer expert, now live in Manhattan Beach, California, and travel frequently.

Previous Titles

LADY CARO
THE DUKE'S REVENGE
THE RELUCTANT HEIRESS

THE NOTORIOUS MARQUESS

Marlene Suson

MILLS & BOON LIMITED
ETON HOUSE   18-24 PARADISE ROAD
RICHMOND   SURREY   TW9 1SR

First published in Great Britain 1989 by Mills & Boon Limited

© Marlene Suson 1988

Australian copyright 1989
Philippine copyright 1990
This edition 1990

ISBN 0 263 76727 2

Set in Times Roman 11 on 12 pt.
04-9002-61554 C

Made and printed in Great Britain

CHAPTER ONE

WHEN the stage from the north pulled into London, a woman was among the four unfortunate souls seated on the vehicle's roof. Although she was a gaunt, pale creature with black circles beneath weary blue eyes, the burly, bewhiskered coachman eyed her admiringly as he helped her down. She had pluck, she did, to be travelling alone, and on an outside seat at that. It took real courage to ride on that precarious perch. Only a slender iron railing a few inches above the seat protected the passengers from sliding off. When the stage swayed around curves or careened down hills, it was not easy to retain one's position. Yet he had not heard so much as a murmur of either fear or protest from the poor woman, whom he judged to be in her late twenties. It must have been the most frightening experience of her life, and he offered his commiseration.

'Oh, I have had worse journeys,' she replied cheerfully. Her voice had a startlingly rich, husky timbre, and the warmth of her smile made her suddenly seem pretty. It was beyond the coachman's comprehension how she could still smile after what she had endured, and he told her so.

'I am only grateful that it is summer,' she replied lightly. 'I am told that people have frozen to death riding on outside seats in the winter.'

'Aye, and so they 'ave,' he admitted.

When her feet were upon the ground, the coachman, who was not a short man, was surprised to see that the woman stood as tall as he did. She looked so thin and delicate that he had assumed she was much shorter. Her hair had been pulled severely back from her thin face and hidden so well beneath a black poke bonnet that he could not tell its colour. Both her bonnet and her black bombazine gown, a much-altered relic from an earlier era, were dulled by a film of dust acquired during the journey.

Despite her shabby, outmoded clothes, she had an unconscious aura of breeding and authority about her. The coachman prided himself on recognising quality when he saw it. He was not as blind as his two other female passengers, the fat wife of a village merchant and her equally fat daughter, who had occupied two of the more expensive inside seats. They had refused to breakfast in the same room with a woman who could afford only an outside seat.

The black-clad woman claimed a leather portmanteau that although scuffed and worn from long use must have cost a handsome sum new. The coachman watched as she picked up her bag, squared her weary shoulders, and set resolutely off on foot even though she was clearly burnt to the socket from her exhausting trip. He wondered who she was. No matter what her present circumstances, there was good blood in that 'un.

He would have been shocked to learn how good, for she was Lady Annabelle Smythe, daughter of a distinguished Earl and granddaughter of an even more distinguished Duke. Members of the *ton* with memories that stretched back beyond a decade could have told the coachman that Lady Belle, as she had been known, had been just that, the belle of her coming-out Season. She had received a number of flattering offers for her hand, all of which she had refused. Despite her popularity, she had not, even then, been a beauty, and her rejection of some of the *ton*'s most eligible young men had given rise to the rumour that Lady Belle thought too highly of herself. The rumour was false. Annabelle had spurned the offers not because she overvalued her own worth but because none of the suitors had captured her heart.

Now, lugging her portmanteau, she headed wearily towards Berkeley Street, past mansions where once she had danced the night away. Her black bombazine dress was far too heavy for such a hot, still day as this, and she longed for a cooling breeze to spring up.

She trudged up Piccadilly past Devonshire House, its rather simple exterior giving little hint of the splendidly opulent interior designed by William Kent. Hary-O, daughter of the fifth Duke of Devonshire, had been one of Annabelle's closest friends during her three seasons in London before she had gone to live in the West Indies with her father. A wistful smile tugged at Annabelle's lips as she recalled the gala farewell party that had been held for her at Devonshire House when she had left for Barbados.

Turning off Piccadilly on to Berkeley Street, Annabelle could not help but reflect upon how far she had fallen, thanks to one man, from those golden days to her current condition.

And now she was about to confront that man— her half-brother Frederick. She had not much hope that it would improve her situation, but she had to try.

A troubled frown creased her brow as she thought of Frederick, the sole issue of her father's disastrous second marriage. Annabelle and her half-brother, who at twenty-two was seven years her junior, were as unlike as the mothers who had produced them. One had been sunny and open, the other cold and devious.

Frederick had succeeded to the title of Earl of Chilton upon the sudden and unexpected death of his father the previous year. A weak, cowardly youth who commanded no respect in his own right, Frederick gloried in the power and privilege that his new rank bequeathed upon him. He was odiously rude, condescending, even bullying to his social inferiors and even more odiously obsequious to his betters.

But worse, there was a streak of cruelty in Annabelle's half-brother that deeply disturbed her. Frederick seemed to revel in exercising capricious authority over his tenants, his servants, and, most of all, over his half-sister.

Their father's will had unwittingly given Frederick absolute control over her large inheritance and, thereby, over Annabelle herself. How painful it was after years of being, in effect, her own mistress, to find herself suddenly at the mercy of a stranger's dictatorial whims. And Frederick was a stranger. Until six months ago Annabelle had seen her half-brother no more than four times in her life, the last being when he was a bandy-legged boy of nine.

His warring parents had separated shortly after his birth, and his mother had kept him with her in London. His father had lived at Hillbrook, his country seat in Cambridgeshire, with Annabelle, the child of his first and far happier marriage. There had been no opportunity for fraternal affection to develop between the half-sister and brother. Nor, for that matter, for the intense animosity that Frederick clearly harboured for Annabelle. She wondered, as she had so often, what had spawned it.

After her father's death she had begged Frederick in vain for a little money from her large inheritance to set up a modest household in London. He had summarily rejected her pleas, saying that the only unmarried women with their own London establishments were eccentrics, and he would not permit a sister of his to so embarrass his family's proud name.

She had refused to take no for an answer, however, and at last he had told her that he would permit her to have her own household, but only at Moorlands. She had been surprised by his choice, because Moorlands was not one of the large estates that she had inherited but instead was a small entailed property in Yorkshire that belonged to her brother. Annabelle had been so desperate to escape the unpleasant company of Frederick and his wife, Hetty, that she had agreed. She would not have done so had she ever seen Moorlands.

Annabelle vividly remembered her shock when Frederick's coachman had deposited her there and hastily driven off before she could climb back into the carriage. It had been the dreariest, loneliest place she had ever seen, isolated on the bleak Yorkshire moors miles from its nearest neighbour and many more miles from a village. The house itself had been in sad disrepair. She could think of no reason why Frederick would have wanted to exile her there except a cruel desire to demonstrate his absolute power over her.

Well, he had sadly misjudged his sister if he had thought she would bow meekly to him. His behaviour made her only more determined to find a way to wrench control of her inheritance from him. She would need help, however, and there was no one for her to turn to but her cousin Jean-Louis, now the Comte de Vergennes. He would surely aid her, but Annabelle had lost track of him during the long years of war between his nation and hers. After Napoleon had abdicated and retired to the island

of Elba the preceding April and the French mon-
archy had been restored, she had hoped that Jean-
Louis would write to her. But she had heard nothing
from him. She did not even know whether he was
still alive.

Annabelle, hot and weary after her long walk
from the stage stop, at last reached the Earl of
Chilton's fashionable London residence in Berkeley
Street. Her brother's travelling carriage, the same
one that had transported her to Moorlands, was
waiting outside with a small trunk and several port-
manteaux strapped to the top. Annabelle, wondering what trip was in the offing, clanged the
ornate brass knocker. The door was answered by
an austere, middle-aged butler whom she did not
recognise.

Beyond him, beside a tulipwood table with
ormulu mounts and cabriole legs, stood
Frederick's wife, Hetty, a plump, cow-eyed young
woman attired in a lavender muslin gown. The cut
of the dress, although in the first stare of fashion,
emphasised her short, dumpy body, and its colour
made her look decidedly jaundiced. It had surprised Annabelle that Frederick, always so full of
his own consequences, should have deigned to
marry Hetty, who not only lacked beauty and
liveliness but was of decidedly inferior breeding.

Acutely sensitive about her birth, the young
Countess loudly espoused the most rigid, narrow
standards of propriety as proof of her superior
character. Her conversation was generally devoted
to scandalised dissections of the moral failings of

others, which she invariably began with the phrase, 'I was never so shocked...' Hetty's effort to enhance her own consequence by tearing down everyone else's in a tone of condescending superiority exasperated Annabelle, who had a broader experience of the world and a more compassionate view of human frailty.

Hetty, seeing her sister-in-law, blurted out, 'How did you get here? Frederick will be so angry when he sees you!'

Annabelle did not doubt that in the slightest, but she enquired calmly, 'Is he home?'

'He is about to leave. Lord Chapman has invited him to a house party at Budwell Abbey.'

The invitation surprised Annabelle as much as it must have delighted her brother. Despite his assiduous and obsequious courting of the more exalted members of the *ton* like Lord Chapman, Frederick, for some reason, was shunned by them. Perhaps he was at last winning the acceptance that he so desperately coveted.

'Do you not go with him?' Annabelle asked his wife.

'I wanted to,' Hetty said with a pout, 'but only men are invited.'

His sister doubted that was the case, despite what Frederick had told his wife. Annabelle had discovered that her brother was inclined to say whatever suited him no matter how far from the truth, and she strongly suspected that he had not wanted to take Hetty with him. His indifference to his wife was apparent to everyone except the Countess herself.

'Frederick should be down in a few minutes,' Hetty said. 'We can wait for him in the drawing room.'

Following her sister-in-law into the designated room, Annabelle checked abruptly on its threshold. The classic furnishings that had made it so handsome when her father had been Earl were gone, replaced by a clutter of imitation Chinese pieces made of beech that had been painted yellow to look like bamboo. The walls had been redone with Chinese paper, hand-painted in brilliant, if clashing, colours. For one stunning instant Annabelle wondered if she had somehow been transported into that monument of exotic excess, the Regent's pavilion at Brighton.

'Isn't the room lovely?' Hetty asked. 'Frederick himself chose all the furniture and oversaw every detail. It was quite expensive. I own I was amazed that he would spend so much, but he said that an Earl must live in surroundings befitting his title.'

Annabelle thought them more befitting an eastern despot than an English Earl. How like Frederick to waste his money on an ugly, ostentatious drawing room in the belief that it would further his own consequence while he begrudged his servants a living wage and refused to advance his half-sister so much as a shilling from her *own* inheritance to buy mourning clothes. Although Frederick would happily expend vast sums on his own comforts and amusements, he was shockingly clutch-fisted when it came to anyone or anything else.

When the sisters-in-law were seated upon one of the Chinese sophas, Annabelle said, 'Tell me about the illuminations and fireworks celebrating Napoleon's banishment to Elba. I would have so liked to see them.'

But Hetty had no interest in such frivolities as illuminations and fireworks celebrating peace when there was moral degeneracy to be denounced. She launched instead into a scandalised chronicle of the shocking behaviour of Lady Caroline Lamb and her former lover, Lord Byron.

Finally exhausting even that fertile subject, Hetty moved on to another, saying, 'I was never so shocked, Annabelle, as to learn that your old governess, Claire Potter, has joined the muslin company.'

'What nonsense, Hetty!' Annabelle protested. 'Claire Potter is a pattern of propriety!'

Indeed, Claire, despite much adversity, was as good a woman as Annabelle had ever known. The well-educated daughter of a respectable but impoverished family, Claire had married a young naval officer whom she had adored. Although he had had no money either, he had just assumed command of his own ship, and his financial future had seemed bright. But a few months after the wedding, his ship had gone down at sea before his prospects had been realised, leaving Claire a penniless widow. She had been forced to seek employment as a governess, and Annabelle had been her first charge.

Possessed of a pleasing manner, excellent understanding, and a gentle, loving character, Claire had quickly become more a member of the family than an employee, and Annabelle loved her like an elder sister. Claire had remained with her former charge as a friend and companion until Annabelle and her father had left England eight years before to live on his plantation in the West Indies. Claire was terrified of venturing upon the sea, and she had sought another position in England.

Poor Claire. A year ago her mother, to whom she was deeply devoted, had become an invalid, and Claire had been determined to keep her parent with her. But she had been unable to find an employer who would permit a governess to bring a burdensome invalid into his house. So Claire had used her meagre savings to start a small school for girls, but it had failed to prosper, and she had been forced to close it at the end of last term. Then Lord Ellerton, whom gossips called the Notorious Marquess, had asked her to become governess for his sixteen-year-old half-sister, Lady Rachel Hartley. Although Claire had known that accepting his employ would do her reputation no good, his lordship had generously offered to let her mother live with her beneath his roof. Claire, who by then was in desperate financial straits, had accepted the position.

Hetty said with a sniff, 'You will be as shocked as I was when I tell you that Mrs Potter is living with that infamous libertine, Lord Ellerton, at his home in Berkeley Square.'

'Not, however, as his convenient,' Annabelle said icily. 'That is an unconscionable slander of Claire!'

'Is it? Then why is she running off to Paris with him?'

'Claire is going to Paris!' She had written to Annabelle of her reasons for accepting Ellerton's employ, but she had said nothing about a journey to Paris. Knowing Claire's dread of the sea, Annabelle was surprised that she could have been persuaded to cross the Channel, but most likely Ellerton had given the poor thing no choice. If Claire were truly going to France, however, she might be able to locate Jean-Louis for Annabelle. Concealing her excitement over this possibility, she asked, 'When does Claire leave?'

Hetty gave another loud sniff. 'In a day or two. So shocking!'

'Does Ellerton's half-sister, Lady Rachel Hartley, also accompany them to France?' Annabelle enquired acidly.

'It does not signify. No woman's reputation can survive a journey under the Notorious Marquess's protection,' Hetty said in a tone of such grating superiority that Annabelle had a strong urge to throttle her.

'Don't be such a peagoose, Hetty! Claire's position as Lady Rachel's governess is perfectly respectable. The Hartleys are an old and distinguished family.'

'A distinguished family until the current Marquess disgraced it with that dreadful scandal involving Lord Ivly's poor daughter!' the young Countess said with another disapproving sniff.

Leave it to Hetty to dredge up ancient history. 'That was nearly twenty years ago,' Annabelle said coldly.

'The stories they tell about him are shocking,' Hetty exclaimed.

That was true enough. It would be hard to say which was more censured: Ellerton's manners or his morals. According to all reports, he cared not the slightest whom he offended. Noted for his sarcastic wit, he did not scruple to speak his mind with a frankness that was always disconcerting and sometimes uncivil. Having heartlessly ruined one lady of quality, he professed an insulting aversion for her sisters, openly preferring the muslin company instead. Not that his low taste in women was so different from a number of other men of rank, but instead of behaving discreetly as they did, he had the effrontery to publicly display his convenients of the moment.

'Lord Ellerton's reputation is such that I would not dare be in the same room with him,' Hetty said virtuously.

Since Ellerton ignored even the loveliest ladies of the *ton* and favoured only the most dazzling of the high fliers with his attentions, Annabelle was amused by her dull, unattractive sister-in-law's certainty that he would try to seduce her.

'I do not believe you need worry, Hetty,' she said gently. 'He has no taste for ladies of propriety, only for the most beautiful barques of frailty.'

'They say that he intends never to marry,' Hetty said.

Which, since he must be nearing forty now, was likely true. Despite the scandal involving Lord Ivly's daughter, the Marquess's title and purse were such that a large number of caps belonging to very respectable—and in some cases beautiful—young ladies had been set in vain for him over the years. Instead of redeeming himself after the shocking Ivly affair by marrying an unexceptional young lady of the first respectability, he had compounded his original sin by ignoring all the choicest offerings of the Marriage Mart and flaunting his high fliers in society's face.

Although Annabelle had never met Lord Ellerton, the paradoxes about him intrigued her. Despite his uncongenial reputation, some of the most sought-after demi-reps of the age had vied to live under his protection. Despite his cutting tongue—or perhaps because of it—he had become in recent years part of a select circle of men reputed to be the wittiest and most entertaining in London society. Poor dull Frederick, with his lofty social ambitions, would give anything to be a member of it. Despite the Marquess's disgraceful conduct among the fair sex, he was held to be scrupulously fair and correct in all his dealings with men and quietly generous to friends who had fallen into the River Tick.

Hetty sniffed loudly. 'They say that he actually prefers his lightskirts to the company of respectable women. Not that a respectable woman would associate with him.'

'Then he has no alternative to his lightskirts, does he?' Annabelle observed drily.

Hearing a sound at the drawing room door, she looked up to see Frederick there. Annabelle and her young half-brother were as unlike in appearance as they were in disposition and character. Frederick, so lacking in pluck and dash, was as diminutive and round-shouldered as his mother. And as devious. He had inherited her brown eyes and blond hair while Annabelle favoured their tall, blue-eyed, brown-haired father, who had stood straight and distinguished.

Frederick had embraced the most extreme fashions of the day. His wispy hair had been set in papers to achieve its crown of limp curls. His excessively high collar points and elaborately tied cravat had been starched to a ridiculous stiffness. His mulberry satin waistcoat was heavily embroidered and additionally ornamented with a startling collection of seals and fobs. The cut of his green coat and the skin-tight fit of his fawn pantaloons accentuated his small, unprepossessing body and matchstick legs. Poor Frederick had not the figure for the foppishness he favoured.

As he raised his quizzing glass to examine his wife's visitor, Annabelle was fascinated by the ostentatious collection of jewelled rings that adorned his fingers.

Belatedly recognising Annabelle, he dropped his glass in shock. She could have sworn that for an instant she saw a glint of fear in his eyes.

'How did you get here?' he sputtered. 'You will return to Moorlands at once.'

'No,' she said calmly. He might have control over her, but he would never have the power to intimidate her. 'I prefer to remain in London.'

'You wished to set up your own establishment at Moorlands,' he cried shrilly. 'You have made your bed and now——'

'No, Moorlands was your choice,' she reminded him. '*You* made my bed and now I decline to lie in it.'

His bejewelled fingers plucked nervously at his quizzing glass. 'I will not stand the expense of setting up a new household for you.'

'It is not you who must pay for it. My inheritance is large enough to cover my return to London,' she pointed out, rising from the Chinese sopha to face him. She stood a full five inches taller than he did.

Forced to look up at her, he said uneasily, 'Sit down!'

When she did not comply, he said petulantly, 'What a pity that disgraceful governess of yours did not teach you obedience when you were a child. It is a humiliation to me that a former retainer of my family could have so lowered herself to accept a position with a man of such shocking repute as Lord Ellerton.' Frederick's lips curled in a sneer. 'He is not received in polite society.'

'To the contrary,' Annabelle said sweetly, 'I understand that he is very popular among that segment of the *ton* which prefers wit to propriety.'

Frederick glared at her. 'But that is not the very best circle.'

'Only the most enjoyable and the most envied,' Annabelle retorted, knowing how much her half brother yearned to be part of it.

'Ellerton is the rudest, most detestable man I have ever met,' Frederick said with such loathing Annabelle knew immediately that something unpleasant had occurred between Ellerton and her half-brother. From the heat of Frederick's reaction, she was inclined to think that it had been more serious than his having merely been the target of the Marquess's caustic tongue.

'He doesn't scruple to say the most outrageous, uncivil things, and cares not at all what the *ton* thinks of him,' continued Frederick, who clearly found Ellerton's disregard for such august opinion beyond his comprehension. 'Why, he holds Brummell's or even Prinny's opinion of no account.'

'Wise man,' Annabelle murmured irreverently. Beau Brummell was, in her opinion, an insufferable snob and the Prince Regent a fat fool.

'And it is sickening the vast sums of money he squanders on his lightskirts!'

Knowing how clutch-fisted Frederick was when it came to anyone but himself, Annabelle was not surprised that he should be more outraged by Lord Ellerton's generosity than by his morals.

'Mrs Potter has put herself beyond the pale by accepting that rakeshame's employ,' Frederick snapped. 'As for you, you will return on the morrow to Moorlands.'

'Why are you so determined to keep me at Moorlands?'

The uneasiness in his eyes told Annabelle that he had a reason, but he evaded her question. 'You will do as I say.'

'No, I shall not,' Annabelle said firmly.

'I shall make you.'

'Do you mean to bind and gag me and thrust me into your carriage?' she enquired calmly. 'For you shall get me there no other way.'

Her defiance clearly left him at a loss to know what to do. Nervously he pulled out his watch and, looking at it, complained, 'You could not have picked a worse time to descend upon me. I must leave immediately.' He seemed to puff up before her eyes as he continued gloatingly. 'I have been invited to Budwell Abbey, Lord Chapman's country seat, for a house party.'

When Annabelle did not seem nearly so impressed as he was by this invitation, he said peevishly, 'We will discuss your future when I return on Monday.'

'I want to know why you are so determined to keep me at Moorlands,' Annabelle repeated.

Again, the unease she had seen earlier flickered in Frederick's eyes. He turned and hurried out of the room without answering her.

CHAPTER TWO

CLAIRE POTTER, her face reflecting the strain of
the seemingly endless night that she had spent, rose
wearily from the bedside of her gravely ill mother,
now tossing restlessly in a feverish sleep. Claire did
not look in the least like a scandalously employed
woman. Everything about her from the neat style
of her greying hair to the high collar, drab colour,
and full skirt of her gown was conservative.

Needing to stretch her limbs, she walked into the
adjoining sitting room, which, like the bedroom she
had just left, was richly furnished. Two armchairs
with gadroon backs flanked a Hepplewhite settee,
all upholstered in the same jade-green silk that
adorned the windows. A mahogany secretaire with
a swan-neck pediment resided between two long
windows that looked out over an impressive expanse of gardens stretching to the south of Berkeley
Square.

How her poor mother loved that view. Ellerton
House had its own garden, too, abloom with roses
and circular beds of marigolds, pansies, and
begonia. When the weather was good, Lord
Ellerton would have the invalid carried down to it
so that she might sit there. Claire swallowed hard.
She was enormously indebted to the Marquess for
his kindness to her and her mother. This apartment

that he had allocated to them was quite the most elegant quarters they had ever had. And he had instructed his servants to give Claire whatever help she might wish with the invalid. He had been so excessively generous to them. How could she possibly repay him for all he had done by refusing at the last moment to go to France!

A knock, too soft to disturb the sick woman in the bedroom, sounded at the door to the apartment. It was Bridget, one of the maids. 'How be ye mum now?' she asked.

'Worse, I fear,' Claire replied, her voice cracking with emotion.

The young maid's bright eyes clouded unhappily. 'And what will ye do, what with the master and the young lady leavin' and expectin' ye to be going with them?'

It was the same question that had been tormenting Claire since her mother had been stricken during the night. Lord Ellerton was departing this very afternoon for a quick visit to Elmdale, his country seat in Dorset. He would go from there directly to the harbour at Newhaven, where he would set sail for France.

Claire and his half-sister, Lady Rachel, were to leave early the day after tomorrow to meet him at Newhaven and accompany him to France. The prospect of crossing the English Channel had been terrifying enough to Claire, who had feared the sea since it had claimed her husband, but now she faced the possibility that her mother might die while she was gone.

Seeing Claire's stricken look, Bridget said, 'Sure, and I'm thinking that ye best be telling his lordship that ye cannot go. I'm thinking his lordship, if he knew the truth about ye mum, would not want it.'

'But what can he do?' Claire asked in despair. She knew that Lord Ellerton's trip to France was urgent and could not be postponed. 'He leaves this afternoon, and it is too late for him to find someone to take my place.'

'His lordship, he's not a bad man for all the things they say about him. If ye tell him of ye mum's condition, I'm thinking he might leave both ye and his sister at home.'

Claire shuddered to think what vengeance Lady Rachel would exact were she to be thwarted now in her determination to accompany her half-brother to Paris. Claire's lips tightened in distaste as she thought of her spoiled, selfish, spiteful charge. Never in Claire's experience had she met such a sullen, contrary, impossible girl as Lady Rachel, and she was at a loss to know how to deal with her. If the Marquess were to leave her behind, Claire would be responsible for her. That prospect was even more unnerving to Claire than crossing the Channel.

The maid said, 'I'm forgetting why I'm here. Ye have a caller, a Miss Anna B. Smith.' Bridget giggled. 'Quite a start she gave that stiff-necked Thomson when he opened the door and saw a lady standing there all alone. I thought he'd shut the door in her face.'

Who on earth could the woman be? Claire wondered. She knew no Anna Smith. She had not even heard the name Anna in years, not since dear Lady Annabelle's cousin, Jean-Louis, had returned to France. He had always insisted on calling Annabelle that to tease her because he knew she did not like the name. Claire suppressed a gasp. Could it be that her caller was Lady Annabelle Smythe? The momentary joy that Claire felt at the prospect of seeing her former charge quickly gave way to dismay, and she was quite as shocked as Thomson had been. What on earth could have possessed Annabelle to present herself unchaperoned at a London bachelor's door for all the world to see her, but most especially when he was a bachelor of Lord Ellerton's reputation?

What a scandal would erupt if Lady Annabelle Smythe, daughter of the late Earl of Chilton and granddaughter of the Duke of Holton, had been recognised entering, quite alone, the Notorious Marquess's house. Nor did Claire think her employer would like it above half either. However careless he might be of his reputation, no woman, unescorted by her husband, was permitted to call upon him in Berkeley Square. None of his convenients ever dared do so. Claire would have to chastise her former charge for having so little regard for the proprieties.

But when Annabelle was shown into the sitting room a few minutes later, Claire was so startled by how exhausted and unhappy she looked, she forgot to reprimand her. Usually Annabelle was brimming with energy and cheerfulness, but now even her quick, eager step had slowed, betraying a weariness of spirit as well as body. Claire, who had not seen her for several months, wondered whether continuing grief over her father's death a year before was responsible for the alarming change.

Annabelle was still wearing mourning black. She had always dressed with flair, but now she looked shockingly dowdy. Her dreadful bombazine gown had neither flair nor fashion. Indeed, it looked as though it had been retrieved from an attic where it had lain for years, and had been extensively altered to make it more nearly conform to current style.

Although Annabelle had never been a true beauty, she had once been a most striking young woman. Her prettiness, however, had depended on the glowing liveliness of a sunny disposition, an easily provoked sense of humour, and an adventurous spirit. Now, at twenty-nine, that special glow seemed to have vanished, her complexion had lost its bloom, and her most outstanding feature, eyes that were as rich and deep as the blue of the sea on a calm day, were no longer brilliant but dull and weary.

They lit up, however, at the sight of Claire. Embracing her former governess, she exclaimed, 'How wonderful it is to see you!'

At least Annabelle's distinctive voice, so husky and vibrant that one admirer had described it as positively smoky, was unchanged.

'What a lovely sitting room, and the view is splendid,' Annabelle exclaimed, looking through one of the windows towards the view to the south. 'And such pretty gardens. Do they belong to Lansdowne House?'

'The near one does,' Claire replied. 'Beyond it is the garden of Devonshire House. You know how dearly Mama loves gardens. Lord Ellerton gave us this apartment expressly so that she could see them. He has been kindness itself to us.'

Such thoughtfulness did not square with the Notorious Marquess's reputation for cavalier treatment of women, and Annabelle said, 'I own I am astonished. From all that is said about him, one would think he had no heart at all.'

'I think his manner discomfits people,' said Claire, who was one of those discomfited souls, made uneasy, despite his lordship's kindness, by his abruptness and his sardonic remarks. 'You should not have come here unchaperoned, Annabelle. Surely, you must know Lord Ellerton's reputation.'

Annabelle smiled. 'I doubt there is anyone in England who does not!'

'Think what a scandal there will be if you were recognised entering here.'

'Dear Claire, you refine too much. No one would know me after all these years, especially not dressed like this. And I had to come. I desperately need your help! Is it true that you leave soon for France?'

'I am scheduled to go day after tomorrow, but——'

'Would you try to find my cousin Jean-Louis while you are there?' Annabelle interrupted eagerly. For a moment the old glow rekindled in her eyes.

'Oh, Claire, how lucky you are! I have yearned to go to France since I was a little girl, listening to Grand'mère and Tante Marie and Jean-Louis talk of it. Papa meant to take me there in '03 during the Peace of Amiens, but it was so short-lived that we lost the opportunity.'

Claire, who was not feeling in the least lucky, cried, 'If only you could go instead of me! Mama is very ill. She was stricken during the night, and I cannot bear to leave her.' A film of tears misted her eyes. 'Oh, Annabelle, I fear that I will never see her again. She will die while I am gone!'

'And Ellerton still insists that you go?' Annabelle cried hotly. 'You call that kind?'

'You do him an injustice. I have not told him that she is ill.'

'Why not?'

'Because Lady Rachel must have a companion, and there is no time for him to find a replacement for me. He leaves this very afternoon, and we are to meet him at the coast the day after tomorrow. He has been so kind to us that I cannot leave him in the lurch now.' Claire sank down on the jade-green settee.

'Why would Ellerton wish to take his sister with him anyway? I cannot conceive of any bachelor, particularly one of his reputation, wanting to saddle himself with a schoolroom miss in Paris.'

'He does not want her with him,' Claire explained, gesturing to Annabelle to sit beside her on the settee. 'In the beginning he absolutely refused to take her. But she was determined to go, and I doubt that she has ever failed to get her way in her life. She swears that if she is left behind, she will elope with Eustace Walford, who *will* take her to Paris.'

'Has she no more discrimination than a fortune-hunting fribble who is still a calfling!' Annabelle scoffed as she sat down beside Claire.

'You are acquainted with him?'

'Only by reputation. Every one of his four older brothers was a gazetted fortune hunter, a slowtop, and a vain fop in the bargain, and I have heard that Eustace is by far the most handsome and brainless of the lot. During my come-out Season, his eldest brother dangled after me and every other young lady suspected of commanding an income of more than five thousand a year.'

'I don't remember you mentioning him.'

'He was not worth mentioning! I never met a sillier, more inept paperskull. I sent him packing quick enough, and he never bothered me again. I wish that Lord Garthorpe had been so easy to discourage.' Annabelle could not repress a small shudder at the memory of that excessively handsome, excessively unprincipled man. Blond and fair, he had been likened in his younger days to a Greek god. The only blemish on his perfect countenance was a small birthmark at the corner of his mouth, but he had turned even that into an asset by covering it with a rakish patch. Although very much married, he had made a career of seducing ladies of quality.

Annabelle said thoughtfully, 'I suspect my mistake was to tell him immediately that I wanted nothing to do with him. After that, he regarded me as a challenge.'

'Few ladies could resist Garthorpe when he turned his full charm on them,' Claire observed.

'Which is why he reputedly has planted his bastards in half the great houses of England.'

'Annabelle!' Claire cried in shock. 'You must not talk so.'

Annabelle shrugged. 'It is the truth. At least the eldest Walford was not of Garthorpe's kidney. The worst of the Walford brothers was the third one, Nugent.'

'The one that eloped with Maria Glennell?'

Annabelle nodded. 'Her papa had far loftier ambitions for her and her twenty thousand a year than a penniless Walford. Mr Glennell paid Nugent an exorbitant sum to withdraw his attentions and maintain absolute silence about his flight with Maria. The poor girl was left with a clouded reputation and a broken heart. But enough of this ancient history. What is Lady Rachel like?'

Claire's accumulated frustrations with her charge welled up, and she cried angrily, 'Impossible! I have never met such a provoking, baffling creature in my life! She is impertinent and contrary and refuses to do anything that I ask her. Indeed, I have never met another girl like her.'

'And hope you never will again!' Annabelle guessed.

Claire nodded ruefully. 'Were it not for the Marquess's kindness to Mama and me, I should have given notice by the third day. I have been her governess less than a month now, but it seems like a century. She refuses even to do her lessons. She reads nothing but Gothic novels of the calibre of *The Prisoner of Iago*, and she delights in tormenting me by putting spiders in my bed.'

'I would quickly end that,' Annabelle said.

'What am I to do? She, of course, denies that she is to blame.'

'And I would deny that I was to blame for the cow itch in her bed.'

Claire burst out laughing. 'You wouldn't!' But she knew that Annabelle would. Once when her cousin Jean-Louis had put a frog in her bed, she had retaliated by sprinkling his with the powder that had caused him intolerable itching.

'Rachel sounds like an insufferable, spoiled brat,' Annabelle observed. 'Perhaps she deserves a Walford.'

'If she takes it into her mind to elope, I do not think that anyone except Lord Ellerton himself could prevent her from doing so. That is why he is taking her to Paris. He dares not leave her behind.'

'Ellerton should let Lady Rachel carry out her threat,' Annabelle said thoughtfully. 'I suspect she would quickly regret it. She would be very happy to be rescued from her folly before the knot was even tied.'

'But with the Marquess in France, there would be no one to go after her,' Claire pointed out.

'Why did Ellerton take her under his roof rather than making another arrangement for her? I can think of no more unsuitable guardian for a young lady of sixteen.'

'He himself expressed that same opinion to me, but he had no alternative. She is his ward. After her mother died a few months ago, he placed Lady Rachel with her maternal aunt. But she ran such a careless establishment and exerted so little control over the girl that the Marquess was forced to remove her. Lady Rachel is still sulking about it.'

'How do she and her brother get along?'

'She says that she hates him, and there is no doubt that she's terrified of him.'

Annabelle frowned. 'Has he given her reason to be?'

'None that I know of. He simply ignores her. But he has such a curt, forbidding manner about him.' Indeed, Claire had some sympathy with her aggravating charge on this score. 'He is a very intimidating man.'

Annabelle smiled affectionately at Claire. 'I think you are also a little intimidated by him.'

'Yes,' Claire admitted. 'He is so abrupt, and I am not certain how to take some of the things he says. Did you ever meet him when you were on the town?'

'No,' Annabelle replied. 'The Notorious Marquess was not deemed an acceptable acquaintance for an innocent young female of the first respectability like myself. But I would have had to be deaf not to have heard the scandalous stories that circulated about him.'

'I truly think the tales told about him must be exaggerated,' Claire said earnestly.

'Papa said the same thing,' Annabelle recalled thoughtfully, remembering how her father had once told her that he thought the full story of the Ivly affair had not been told. Ellerton did not strike him as a man who would shirk his duty like that. 'Papa was very fond of Ellerton, which surprised me, for he normally abhorred libertines.'

'Your papa was not often fooled about a man's character,' Claire said.

For a minute the two women sat in silence on the jade settee, each lost in her separate thoughts.

Suddenly Claire burst out miserably. 'I cannot bear to go to France and leave Mama!'

'Nor shall you!' The mischievous gleam of old shone again in Annabelle's eyes. 'I have hit upon the most wonderful scheme! I will go in your stead!'

'You are mad!' Claire gasped, horrified.

'Not at all! Don't you see, it is the perfect solution to both our problems. You can remain with your mother, and I will be able to look for Jean-Louis.'

'It would be unthinkable for the Marquess to employ a lady of your birth and breeding and fortune as a governess. People would immediately assume it was a charade to disguise that you had become his incognita. He is not so ramshackle as that, particularly where his sister is concerned. He would never agree to hire you.'

'No, I daresay he would not if he knew that he was doing so,' Annabelle said cheerfully. 'But he will not know. I will become Miss Anna Smythe instead of Lady Annabelle. He never saw me when I was on the town. Even if he had, I am certain that he would not recognise me now.'

Claire sincerely doubted that anyone would know Annabelle now, so changed was she. Still, the scheme was madness.

'When he sees how young you are, he will instantly reject you,' Claire argued. 'Indeed, the only thing that gave him pause about hiring me was he thought me too young, and I am more than a decade older than you. Furthermore, he said only a widow was acceptable. He would not have an ape leader. Not that you are that,' she added hastily.

'Of course I am at my age,' Annabelle said cheerfully. 'But do not worry. I will persuade Ellerton to hire me.'

In vain did Claire point out what a great scandal would arise should it ever be discovered that the Lady Annabelle Smythe, daughter of the late Earl of Chilton and granddaughter of the Duke of Holton, had travelled to Paris with the Notorious Marquess in the guise of his sister's governess. It would put Annabelle beyond the pale.

She, however, was unperturbed, assuring Claire that she would be a stranger in a strange land, where no one but her cousin Jean-Louis, should she be fortunate enough to locate him, would know her.

'But if your true identity ever be exposed,' Claire argued desperately, 'we would have involved Lord

Ellerton in a terrible scandal. He will be beside himself with fury.'

'Oh, pooh! The Notorious Marquess wouldn't care in the slightest. What is one more scandal to him? This is a man who openly flaunts his high fliers in front of the world. If he learns of our deception, he will most likely think it a great joke.'

A knock sounded at the sitting room door, and Bridget called, 'His lordship, he's wanting to see you in the book room, Mrs Potter. He says not to be keeping him waiting, for he's leaving for Dorset.'

'Tell him that I will go in your place,' Annabelle hissed at Claire.

'I dare not,' the frightened Claire whispered, rising from the settee. 'Why are you so eager to find Jean-Louis that you would set about it in such a ramshackle fashion?'

'It will take too long to explain, and you must not keep Ellerton waiting. I will tell you everything after you have seen him.'

'I cannot ask him——'

'Of course you can. Now, don't keep him waiting. You and I will both benefit if he agrees.'

Claire could not argue that point. And she suspected that Lady Rachel would benefit, too. Annabelle had a rare gift for handling difficult people and might know just how to deal with that maddening, headstrong girl.

'At least ask the Marquess?' Annabelle urged.

Reluctantly, Claire acquiesced, confident that he would turn her down without even giving Annabelle an interview. As Claire went to the door, she warned pessimistically, 'It is a waste of time. He will never agree to you.'

'I will convince him to take me,' Annabelle said.

Despite her former charge's remarkable talent for managing people, Claire was firmly convinced that the Marquess was beyond even Annabelle's ability.

CHAPTER THREE

CLAIRE'S knees were quaking as she descended the stairs, and her conscience plagued her. She vowed that under no circumstance would she tell Lord Ellerton an outright lie, but it was still necessary for her to deceive him, by omission rather than commission, about Annabelle's true identity. This troubled Claire greatly. He had been so kind to her and her mother that she despised the prospect of repaying him with deceit.

When Claire entered the library, the Marquess stood with one foot, encased in a handsome leather riding boot, resting negligently on the fender of the fireplace.

His height was intimidating. He stood four inches above six feet and was powerfully built, although at first glance he looked deceptively lean. His chestnut-brown riding coat and buckskin breeches were of the finest material, but their cut and the indifferent arrangement of his neckcloth indicated a man who, although he insisted upon quality in his clothes, cared more for comfort than fashion.

His glittering grey eyes were staring broodingly through one of the tall rectangular windows that looked out on the garden. His hard face, dark and lean with an aquiline nose and sardonic mouth, was partially shadowed, making it appear even harsher than usual. Although he was eight and thirty, his unruly hair was thick as a schoolboy's and black as the unlit coal in the grate by his feet.

He stepped away from the fireplace, and Claire saw that his thick brows were knited together in a fierce frown. He looked so unapproachable that her legs trembled even more violently beneath the gathers of her long grey skirt. She suddenly found herself bereft of both the words and the courage to propose to him that Annabelle go in her place to France.

She was rescued, however, by his saying brusquely, 'I have just learned that your mother is very ill. Of course you must remain here with her, although I do not know what the deuce I am to do about Rachel.'

His unconsciously curt manner detracted from the kindness of his declaration, but Claire was, nevertheless, touched by it. 'I believe that I can offer you a solution, my lord,' she stammered. 'I have a dear friend who is in need of a position and would be happy to accompany Lady Rachel to France. She is even now in my apartment upstairs.'

'Who is she?'

'Her name is—uh—Anna...Anna Smythe, my lord,' Claire said, acutely conscious that, while this was not exactly a falsehood, neither was it the whole truth.

'I hope this Anna Smith is not as common as her name,' he said in the abrupt manner of his that made Claire ill at ease with him.

She refrained from telling him that this Anna was one of the distinguished Smythes, not the common Smiths, even though the names were pronounced the same. Instead, she said, 'The Smythes are an old and well-respected family in Cambridgeshire.' Which was certainly true. None was older or more respected.

The Marquess scowled, and Claire thought in dismay that he meant to refuse Annabelle.

She would have been relieved to know that his lordship's frown was prompted less by his reaction to her proposal than by the coil he found himself in. He could not postpone his journey to France. His business there would not permit it, and he must sail two days from now as scheduled. All preparations for the voyage had been carried out. An overburdened wagon carrying the baggage for the trip had departed for Newhaven that morning so that everything could be stowed aboard his yacht well in advance of sailing.

He himself must leave immediately for Elmdale, his country seat in Dorset, where he would spend the morrow, Friday, giving final instructions for its management during his absence in France. Early on Saturday, his half-sister, her maid, and Mrs Potter were to depart in his trusted Putney's custody for Newhaven. Drawn by his fastest horses with frequent changes along the way, their coach would reach the coast in the afternoon. He would ride directly from Elmdale to Newhaven to meet them, and they would weigh anchor for France that same day, catching the evening tide.

He faced hard hours in the saddle in order to reach Elmdale tonight, and he was eager to be on his way. But first he would have to deal with the unexpected complication of Rachel's governess being unable to accompany them.

The most expedient thing for him to do would be to substitute this Anna Smith, but he did not like above half taking with him a governess whose credentials he had not had time to check thoroughly.

On the other hand, he trusted Mrs Potter more than he did any other woman. He had been moved by her gentleness and honesty, and by her deep and unselfish devotion to her mother, so unlike other women of his acquaintance, who gave of themselves only in proportion to the gain it brought them.

Claire said eagerly, 'Anna is a mature, genteel lady, well bred and well educated. Not only is she a model of propriety, but she speaks French fluently. Indeed, I am persuaded that she will be perfect for Lady Rachel, better by far than I.'

His lordship gave her a sharp look. 'Why do you say that?'

'I fear I am at a loss to know how to deal with your sister,' Claire confessed.

No more than I, Ellerton thought wearily. What the devil did a bachelor of his years and predilections know about raising a spoiled schoolroom brat? But he appreciated Mrs Potter's honesty. It was one of the things he most liked about her.

'Anna has a rare talent for dealing with difficult people,' Claire said. 'I am persuaded that she will be better able to control your sister than I am.'

'I doubt a woman exists who can control Rachel,' his lordship said. Certainly neither her mother, her aunt, nor her long line of governesses had been able to. 'But I sincerely hope that your Anna Smith can prove me wrong.'

He feared, however, that the woman sounded too good to be true. He had had enormous difficulty securing a proper governess for Rachel. Those women willing to take such a position under the Notorious Marquess's roof he would not have; and those he would have would not accept his employ.

He regarded Claire suspiciously. 'If this Anna Smith is the paragon you say she is, why would she accept a position that requires her to travel to France in the company of the Notorious Marquess?' He was well aware of what the world called him behind his back.

'For the same reason that I did,' Claire replied with quiet dignity. 'She is desperate.'

'I see,' Ellerton said, amused by Mrs Potter's unflattering but honest answer. 'Her late husband left her poorly provided for?'

'Anna had no husband,' she said anxiously. 'She was devoted to her father and never married.'

'What?' he exclaimed angrily. 'You know that I won't have an ape leader! Only a mature widow like yourself is acceptable to me.'

'You will find Anna a most responsible, mature woman,' Claire said nervously.

'I will not be saddled with a timid, vaporish spinster who will get seasick at the mere sight of my yacht!'

'You do Anna a great injustice. She is neither timid nor vaporish. Indeed, she is a far better and braver traveller than I am.'

'You seem very well acquainted with her. How do you know her?'

Claire looked uneasy. 'I...I met her when I went to work for the late Earl of Chilton at his estate in Cambridgeshire. Her father had a handsome property there.'

Ellerton knew of no squire named Smith in that area, but he was not well acquainted with the gentry there. Clearly, however, this Anna Smith had to come from a highly respectable family if it was socially intimate with the late Earl's. Ellerton had liked the old Earl, who had been far more interested in philosophy and science than in the usual aristocratic pursuits of gambling and wenching. When they had met at one or another dinner or house party, they had enjoyed some scintillating conversations and lively arguments. The Marquess had missed Chilton when he had left England to live in the West Indies.

Dragging his thoughts from the past back to the subject at hand, Ellerton said, 'You must emphasise to Miss Smith that it will do her reputation no good at all to be in my employ.'

'I have already done so, but she still wishes the position.'

'Very well, I will interview her. Send her down to me immediately. I have no time to waste.'

As Mrs Potter hurried from the room, Ellerton decided that it was too much to hope that Miss Smith would prove to be neither vaporish nor excessively missish. The Marquess could think of nothing more dreadful than to have to shepherd such a woman across the Channel and through France.

In truth, he was surprised that this Miss Smith should have considered the post. Maiden ladies of mature years, good birth and impeccable virtue avoided him as though he were a contagious disease, although, God knew, they had nothing to fear from him. He was equally eager to avoid them and, indeed, all ladies of quality. The devastating disillusionment that he had suffered two decades before had left him with an abiding distrust of such women.

Since then, the only females he had favoured with his attentions were exquisitely beautiful birds of paradise. He had no patience with romantic nonsense, preferring value given for value received. Not only were his convenients skilled at pleasing a man for a price, but that price was in gold and jewels, not in treachery and deceit as that of so-called ladies often was.

When Miss Smith entered the library, the Marquess's first impression was of a weary, gaunt woman, plain-faced and colourless, in a dowdy, dreadfully outmoded black gown. Her hair, which he supposed to be iron grey, was entirely hidden under an unflattering black poke hat. Good God, he thought in dismay, she was the perfect caricature of a withered spinster.

But as she advanced into the room he saw that she was not nearly as old as he had first thought. A flood of anger swept over him as he realised that he had been misled by Mrs Potter. There could be only one thing worse than a timid, vaporish spinster, and that was a timid, *young*, vaporish spinster.

'I was told you were a mature woman,' he snapped.

'But I am,' she replied calmly. She had a lovely smoky voice with a sensual timbre that was at such variance with her thin body and drab appearance that he was momentarily silenced. Almost as surprising as her voice was her height. Most women came to his chest, but she reached his lips.

'You cannot be a day over thirty,' Ellerton rapped out, bestowing upon her his famous scowl, which was guaranteed to cow even the bravest woman.

She was unaffected. 'Maturity is not necessarily a matter of years,' she responded, maddeningly undisturbed by his displeasure. 'I know women in their sixties who act like children.'

And so did he, he thought uncomfortably. He was made even more uncomfortable by the forward way that she was examining him with an eye as critical as he himself had been known to use when inspecting a prospective convenient. The effrontery of this bag of bones was outrageous. 'Are you ill?'

he demanded irritably, determined to disconcert her. 'You are as thin as a pole.'

'How uncivil of you to say so,' she said in an amused tone. 'But then, you are notorious for your incivility.'

'Am I now?' He was so nettled by this impertinent creature that he could not help adding mockingly, a rakish gleam in his eye, 'And I thought I was notorious for other reasons.'

He had expected this dried-up spinster to blush furiously in speechless embarrassment, but instead she assured him affably, 'Oh, yes, for that, certainly but for your rudeness as well.'

It was the Marquess who found himself speechless.

'Now, pray tell,' she continued cordially, 'what does my weight or lack of it have to do with my qualifications as a governess? Are you afraid of being accused of starving me while I am in your employ, my lord?'

Her amusement prodded Ellerton's already exacerbated temper. 'You will not be in my employ!' he exploded. 'You are unacceptable!' That would shake her out of her maddening coolness!

But it did not. 'You are unreasonable,' she replied calmly. 'I am perfectly acceptable.'

He could not believe her insolence. 'You are not what you were represented to be. I am enormously disappointed.'

Her eyes narrowed, and she replied with a hauteur that astonished him quite as much as her words. 'No more disappointed than I am with you.'

Although the Marquess was not a man to stand on ceremony, he was none the less outraged by this farouche governess addressing him as though she were his equal rather than a supplicant for his employment.

'What did you say?' he demanded in a voice as haughty as hers.

To his indignation, instead of answering him immediately, she resumed her careful scrutiny of him from the toes of his well-polished riding boots upward to the unruly black hair that crowned his head. Finally, she responded. 'For a man of your reputation, you are not at all handsome. Nor charming either. I would have thought a man who has had such a parade of celebrated demi-reps under his protection would have had to be both. But then, you are very rich.'

Never before had Ellerton been exposed to such critical bluntness by any women, and most certainly not by an insignificant governess. Who the devil did this woman think she was? For an instant he glimpsed something fleeting in her eyes that made him strongly suspect that she was being deliberately provocative. Well, she would find that two could play that game, he thought, suddenly intrigued.

'In light of my reputation,' he said coolly, 'I am astonished that you would consider my employ, Anna.' He deliberately employed the familiarity of her first name rather than addressing her respectfully by her surname.

Only a slight narrowing of her eyes betrayed that this deliberate insult had not passed unnoticed, but she said nothing.

'Are you not concerned for your virtue, Anna?' he pressed mockingly, certain that he had at last discomfited her.

Instead, her amused eyes met his squarely. 'No, my lord, not at all.'

Until that moment, the cynical Marquess had thought himself beyond amazement, but he was indisputably amazed. Despite her bold tongue, he had been certain that she was a pattern card of propriety. But her answer, it seemed to him, could have only one meaning. She was brazenly telling him that she was available for whatever services he might want. Well, she had sadly misjudged his taste. It did not run to plain, skinny females, but to the dramatic and the voluptuous. His smile turned decidedly unpleasant. 'What a bold piece you are, proclaiming to me that you have no virtue.'

For an instant her infuriating imperturbability deserted her, and anger flashed in her eyes. But when she spoke it was in a voice so icy that it could have inflicted frostbite. 'My virtue is impeccable, but I am persuaded that it is perfectly safe with you.'

Indeed it was! But he could not resist enquiring mockingly of this maddening woman, 'You know that—despite my reputation?'

'No, because of it. I am not at all in your style.'

Although her words echoed his own thoughts of a moment earlier, he was startled. 'And just what is my style?'

A mischievous smile that made her look suddenly younger and much prettier lighted her face. 'Dazzling birds of paradise.'

Her accuracy surprised a reluctant laugh from him.

'With a taste for trumpery jewels,' she continued.

This time the Marquess recognised the provocative gleam in her eye for what it was. 'Jewels, yes, but trumpery never,' he retorted, amused despite himself. 'I assure you that any jewels of my bestowing are always in the best of taste.'

Looking about the elegantly furnished library, she said thoughtfully, 'I am inclined to accept your assurance.'

For some unfathomable reason he felt as though he had just been paid a high compliment. Although she was thin and plain and looked to be destitute in that ugly, ancient gown, she had about her an unconscious self-assurance and authority, as though she had long been used to giving commands and having them obeyed, that both intrigued and baffled him. He recalled what Mrs Potter had said about her father.

'Why is the daughter of a man with a handsome property in Cambridgeshire seeking a governess's position?'

'After my father's death last year it was discovered that through some unfortunate—ah—mismanagement on his part, I was left with no money.'

She said it matter-of-factly, without the slightest tinge of self-pity in her marvellous voice, and Ellerton admired her for that.

'Tossed from the lap of luxury into the abyss of poverty in one swift stroke,' he said with genuine sympathy, and he felt himself weakening. Perhaps she would do after all. She seemed so well acquainted with his reputation that she must be aware of what her own might suffer if she accepted a position with him. Nevertheless, he felt it his duty to warn her explicitly. 'You would be well advised not to consider my employ,' he began.

Her head jerked up. 'Why?' she asked in an innocent tone that was belied by the sudden teasing light in her eyes. 'Are you trying to tell me that I was wrong, that my virtue *is* in danger?'

He laughed. 'Not at all. I never seduce ladies of quality. As you so astutely discerned, I prefer ladybirds. They are infinitely more entertaining and less bother than women of your kidney.'

'How fortunate for me,' she said cordially.

'Yes, isn't it?' he returned with equal cordiality. He had never met another woman like her, and he could not help but like her spirit, her quick tongue, her superior understanding, and her easy, teasing humour. He was suddenly conscious of what a highly improper conversation he had been having with her. Damn, but she was so amusing to talk to that he quite forgot that she was a lady.

When he apologised a little stiffly for his lapse, she smiled, and he was struck again at how pretty she was when she did so.

'But I like a man who speaks plainly.'

Listening to her warm, slightly husky voice was like drinking the very finest and smoothest brandy. Its richness was at such variance with her drab appearance. 'What an unusual woman you are,' he remarked, a trace of wonder in his voice.

'Why,' she asked, amusement edging that lovely, smoky voice. 'Because I have no designs on either your purse or your bachelorhood?'

He raised his dark brows sceptically.

The humour vanished from her eyes, and she said with that hauteur she had displayed earlier, 'You flatter yourself.'

'No, I do not flatter myself, but only my title and fortune,' he replied, unable to keep the bitterness from his voice. 'As you pointed out earlier, I am very rich. That and my rank is what women find irresistible, not me. I wager that you, too, would find them irresistible were I to throw the handkerchief.'

To his surprise, her eyes were no longer angry but sympathetic. 'I would find them utterly resistible unless I loved you. Not all women are as mercenary as you think.'

'Aren't they?' he asked in a voice haunted by bitter memories. He knew better. God, did he know better! 'Don't try to gammon me that you are different. Only think, an offer from me would mean that you would never again have to be a governess. I cannot imagine that you find it very pleasant devoting your life to other women's brats. And I warn you again that if you accept my employ, you are not likely to have very desirable positions offered you in the future.'

'Does that mean you will take me to France in Claire's place?'

'Yes,' the Marquess said, realising that was what it did mean. He could only hope that Miss Anna Smith would baffle and disconcert his sister as much as she did him. What a pity he could not wait to witness their first meeting. It should prove to be highly amusing. But he had no more time to waste if he were to reach Dorset tonight, and he told Miss Smith so.

'Mrs Potter will introduce you to my sister. You and Rachel will depart for Newhaven early on the day after tomorrow. I will meet you in Newhaven. For God's sake, do not, whatever you do, keep me waiting there or we will miss the tide, and it is imperative that I get to France as quickly as possible! Tell Mrs Potter that she will remain here with her mother. I will leave orders with Thomson that she is to have whatever assistance she requires. Tell her she is not to hesitate to ask for it, although'—his lips twisted in a wry smile—'I know that she will hesitate.'

'Yes, my lord,' Anna said. 'And thank you.'

'You won't thank me after you meet Rachel,' he warned her. 'She is the most aggravating creature on earth. Except for you!'

CHAPTER FOUR

When Claire heard the outcome of Annabelle's interview with Lord Ellerton, she confessed, 'I feared that he would send us packing when he saw how young you were.'

They were again sitting on the jade-green Hepplewhite settee in Claire's apartment, and Annabelle turned to study her old governess with troubled eyes. 'I thought you would be elated that you will be able to remain in England with your mother, but you seem unhappy.'

'I am delighted that I do not have to go to France, but my conscience bothers me about deceiving Lord Ellerton. I am terrified of what will happen if ever you are recognised. There will be such a scandal, and I fear he will never forgive either of us.'

'Dear Claire, I told you that he most likely will not care a groat about being involved in another scandal.'

'When I agreed to talk to him about you, I did not think that you could convince him to take you, but I should have known that you would. You have such a skill at handling people.'

'Everyone except my half-brother,' Annabelle said ruefully.

'What has he done now? I have not yet recovered from my shock at his behaviour when your father died.'

Nor had Annabelle. The late Earl, a man of apparently robust health, had been summoned back to England the previous year from Barbados, where he and Annabelle had been living for seven years. Mr Barbour, the shrewd and devoted old solicitor who had handled the Earl's financial affairs in England for many years, had suffered an incapacitating stroke that precluded him from continuing to work. The Earl had come back to make new arrangements, leaving Annabelle behind to oversee his West Indies plantation. He had planned only a short stay in his native land, but seeing it again, he had realised how much he missed it and decided to remain permanently.

He had written Annabelle from a house party he was attending with his brother in Gloucestershire, instructing her to return to England as soon as she could settle their affairs in Barbados. She had done as he had asked, but had seen no reason for haste. She had spent several weeks packing and getting things in order before boarding a vessel for her homeland, blissfully unaware that her father had died before the ship carrying his letter to her had sailed from England.

An epidemic of typhoid among the Gloucestershire guests had killed several of them, including the Earl and his brother. Annabelle often reflected on the irony that her father, after surviving the rigours of their extensive and not infrequently dangerous travels through the wilds of the Americas, should have met his untimely end at a peaceful party in rural England.

Frederick had not bothered to notify her of their father's and uncle's deaths, saying that he had supposed her to be already en route to England. When at last she had set sail, her ship had been caught in the remnants of a hurricane that had left it battered and far off course. As a result, the voyage to England had taken two miserable months.

When at last she had set foot on her native land after a seven-and-a-half-year absence, it was to the news that her father and her uncle had been dead nearly six months. Annabelle, who had been very close to both men, had been prostrated with grief. Dear Claire had come and remained with her for three days until Frederick had dragged his sister off to Hillbrook.

A huge lump swelled in Annabelle's throat as she considered what a different place Hillbrook had become under the new Earl. When her gregarious father had presided there, the house had always been full of guests, chosen not for their titles and wealth but for their intellect and wit. What a lively time they had all had!

Frederick, however, had but two interests: money and social standing. He had made it very clear to every one of the neighbours with whom she and her father had been friends that he considered himself too far above their touch to associate with them. Nor would he permit his sister to do so either, and she soon came to feel like a prisoner in her old

home. Her brother's snobbery had quickly alien-
ated the neighbourhood, and his abrasive, clutch-
fisted treatment of the estate's servants and tenants
was doing the same to them.

Claire said to Annabelle, 'Pray do take off that
dreadful bonnet. It is so unbecoming on you.'

Annabelle removed the offending bit of apparel,
revealing a shimmering coil of chestnut hair that
had been hidden beneath it.

Claire said, 'You look as though you have been
ill.'

'I am only tired. I arrived but two hours ago from
Yorkshire.'

'Why did you go to Moorlands? It seemed like
such an unlikely place.'

'Had I ever seen it, I would not have gone there.'
Annabelle explained her own disagreement with
Frederick over setting up her own household. 'For
some reason that I cannot fathom, he seems determined to keep me out of London.'

'But why Moorlands? Could you not stay at
Hillbrook?'

'He did not seem to want me there either once
he and Hetty returned to London. Not that I care
much for Hillbrook now that it is Frederick's. You
cannot imagine how changed it is. I never spent
such a dull few months there as in his and Hetty's
company. We had scarcely any visitors. Frederick
thinks himself too good to associate with the local
society. He did invite some of the most élite
members of the *ton* to visit us, but none of them

came. I think he is neither liked nor accepted by them.'

'What is Frederick's wife like?' Claire asked.

'Dreadfully dull and sanctimonious. Her conversation is devoted to the most odious denigrations of others' characters.' Indeed, Annabelle thought wryly that the only good thing about Moorlands had been the relief it provided from Hetty's incessant moralising. 'Oh, Claire, I cannot tell you how happy I am to be going to France and escaping my brother. If only I can find Jean-Louis.'

'I hope you are up to such an arduous journey,' Claire said. 'You look as though the trip from Yorkshire was too much for you.'

'Well,' Annabelle said cheerfully, 'I can attest that outside seats on the stage are quite as uncomfortable as they are reputed to be.'

'Outside seat!' Claire exclaimed, clearly staggered. 'You came to London on the common stage, and on an outside seat at that! Surely you are hoaxing me.'

Annabelle smiled. 'No.'

'But an outside seat! It is so improper—and so very dangerous.'

Amusement flashed in Annabelle's eyes as she thought of some of the journeys, fraught with far more peril, that she had made with her father in the Americas. Then there had been the hurricane on her return voyage to England last year.

'Why did you take an outside seat?' Claire demanded.

'I could not afford an inside one.'

'Now I know you are gammoning me. Your father left you the greater part of his fortune, everything that was not entailed.'

'Yes, but in a trust that leaves its disbursement entirely to the discretion of the trustee, who is Frederick, and he has refused to give me so much as a shilling, even to buy mourning clothes after Papa's death.'

'Is that why you are wearing that awful dress?'

Annabelle nodded. 'I found it in the attic at Hillbrook and altered it. It was one that Tante Marie wore when she was in mourning for her husband.'

'But that was years ago!' Claire exclaimed. 'I never heard of anything so disgraceful. I cannot conceive why your father made Frederick your trustee. Lord Chilton detested your brother.'

'Much as he disliked Frederick, Papa thought that since he would be the head of the family he deserved the courtesy of being named one of my trustees. There were to be three: Frederick, my uncle, and Mr Barbour. Papa intended that Mr Barbour would be the one who would actually handle all of the trust's affairs and that he and my uncle between them would see that Frederick had no say in its management. But Mr Barbour, as you know, suffered a massive stroke early last year.'

Annabelle rose from the settee and walked to one of the long windows with its view of the Lansdowne and Devonshire gardens. 'Unfortunately, when Papa's will was drawn up years ago before we left for the West Indies, he had made no provision for replacing either my uncle or Mr Barbour as trustees, so that left Frederick in total control.'

'Your papa would turn over in his grave if he knew,' Claire said. 'Can you not break the trust?'

'I had hoped to, but Mr Quigg, the solicitor whom Papa selected to take over his affairs from Mr Barbour, assured me that there is no way that I can do so,' Annabelle said, her voice cracking as she recalled how emphatic Mr Quigg had been that Frederick, for the rest of her life, would have absolute control over her inheritance and how it would be spent.

When Annabelle had angrily declined to accept Mr Quigg's opinion on the trust, he had told her in the strongest of terms that she was wasting her time and his. She frowned, remembering how surprised she had been that Papa had selected him as Mr Barbour's successor in handling his affairs, even though Mr Quigg was Mr Barbour's nephew. There was something odd and oily about Quigg that she could not like.

In fact, she had disliked him so much that she had consulted another solicitor, but he had only reiterated what Mr Quigg had said. A woman in her position had no standing in the eyes of the law. Nevertheless, Annabelle was still determined to find some way to break Frederick's control over her. She was of the sanguine persuasion that any obstacle, no matter how difficult, was meant to be overcome, and she would do so in this case. Her best hope was to find Jean-Louis. He would surely help her.

Claire asked, 'Why did your father not leave your inheritance to you outright?'

'I am afraid my father, as advanced as his thinking was in other ways, adhered to the belief that a lady of quality should not have to deal with anything so crass as financial matters,' Annabelle explained. What a dreadful coil her father's good intentions had left her in.

'But that is ridiculous,' Claire protested. 'You had been running his household and overseeing a good many details of his affairs since your schoolroom days.'

'Yes,' Annabelle agreed, a bitter little smile curling the corners of her mouth at the irony of how much responsibility for his affairs that her father had entrusted to her when he had been alive had been denied to her upon his death.

She stared out over the long, lovely stretch of gardens before her towards Devonshire House, thinking sadly of how much had changed since last she had been there. Poor Duchess Georgiana, once so beautiful and vivacious, a legend in her own time, was dead now, and so was her boring husband. Their son, Hart, who had been a shy youth of fifteen when last Annabelle had seen him, had succeeded to the title. As for Annabelle's friend, Hary-O, she had been married for five years now to Lord Granville-Levin.

Claire's soft voice interrupted Annabelle's reminiscences. 'What did you think of Lord Ellerton?'

Annabelle had been, to her surprise, rather staggered by him. First, there was his size. She was tall, but he towered above her. Then there was his face, too harsh to be handsome, with that cynical mouth that looked as though it rarely smiled and eyes the colour of silver and far harder than the metal ever was. When she had first looked into their cold depths, she had been inexplicably shaken. As Claire had warned her, the man was intimidating, indeed he was, and Annabelle was not used to being intimidated.

His manner had angered her initially, but after he had betrayed a sense of humour she had forgiven him much. She had expected him to be insufferably high in the instep, but it had become clear to her that he was not at all enamoured with his own consequence.

'I liked him, and I did not think that I would,' she told Claire truthfully. The scandal involving Lord Ivly's daughter had prejudiced Annabelle against Ellerton. From his dislike of women and his bitter evaluation of his appeal to them, one would have thought that he had been their victim rather than their undoing. Clearly, he distrusted her sex, and she realised guiltily that she was giving him no reason to change his view by deceiving him about her identity. When she had first proposed doing so, she had sincerely believed that it was no more than the Notorious Marquess deserved. She had been convinced, too, that one more scandal, should she be recognised travelling with him, would not bother him in the slightest. But now she suspected that perhaps she was wrong, and that he would be very angry with both her and Claire.

For the first time, Annabelle was having serious misgivings about her audacious scheme.

It did not take Annabelle more than a few minutes after her introduction to Lady Rachel to ascertain that everything Claire had said about the girl was true. She was sullen and spoiled, and something else that Annabelle had not bargained for—an eye-stopping beauty. The neophyte governess groaned as she contemplated the effect this girl-woman was likely to have on French males.

Rachel's hair was as dark and shining as a raven's wing. Her form was slender, but very well-endowed for a girl of sixteen years. Her tempestuous eyes glowed darkly against skin as rich and white as fresh cream. She had a charming little nose, and her delicate rosebud mouth would have deserved the same appellation had it not been, at that moment, twisted in sulky defiance as she regarded Annabelle with undisguised hostility. Her first words were unpromising for their future relationship. 'So you are to be my new jailer.'

Annabelle, knowing the girl was taking her measure, refused to be disconcerted. 'Yes,' she retorted, laughter in her voice, 'I have your chains in my portmanteau.'

Although startled by this unexpected reply, Lady Rachel said defiantly, 'If you are trying to make me afraid of you, I will have my brother send you packing.'

'I dare say that you have no influence with him. But neither have I any wish to make you afraid of me. I have no taste for tyranny.'

Although there was a glimmer of interest in Rachel's dark eyes, her lips twisted in a pout. 'I don't like you.'

'You don't know me well enough to form an opinion.'

'I have never had a governess I liked!'

'There is always a first time for everything,' Annabelle replied, unperturbed.

The girl studied her curiously. Annabelle met her gaze with unruffled composure. She detected uncertainty, nervousness, and acute unhappiness beneath the girl's defiant pose.

'I am astonished my brother approved of you. You are far too young for his tastes. And,' Rachel added insultingly, 'far too old for mine.'

'How fortunate then that I am the perfect compromise between the two of you.'

The girl gave her an appraising look, then said in an ominous voice, 'I am told that spiders are frequently found in governesses' beds in France.'

'How nice,' Annabelle said cordially. 'I am very fond of spiders. My cousin once put a toad in my bed, but he never tried that a second time.'

'Why not?' the girl asked suspiciously.

'He found cow itch excessively unpleasant.'

'What is that?' Rachel demanded, visibly alarmed.

'A powder that comes from a kind of bean and makes one itch intolerably,' Annabelle said pleasantly. 'I will carry it with me to assure against nocturnal visitors.'

The implied threat was not lost on Rachel, and she had nothing to say for a long moment. Then she burst out, 'You can teach me nothing.'

'Of course I cannot if you are so foolish as to refuse to learn.'

This retort brought a glint of anger to Rachel's eyes, and she said with more temper than honesty, 'I no longer have anything to learn.'

'How fortunate for both of us,' Annabelle said cheerfully. 'I look forward to your teaching me, since I still have much to learn.'

Rachel blinked in surprise. 'No governess should dare admit such a thing!'

'Why not?'

'You pronounce yourself incompetent.'

'Nonsense! I pronounce myself wise enough to recognise the truth and honest enough to admit it.'

Suddenly Rachel grinned. 'I can hardly wait to see how you and my brother deal together. I think it will be vastly entertaining.'

Perhaps for Lady Rachel, Annabelle thought nervously, but not, she suspected, for herself, if Lord Ellerton were ever to learn her true identity.

CHAPTER FIVE

ANNABELLE entertained the idea of remaining in Claire's apartment rather than returning, even temporarily, to her brother's house. But she needed to collect her portmanteau. She had been able to stuff so little into it for her trip to London that it hardly seemed worth the risk of going back for it. Except that if she did not, she would have only the dress she was wearing for the journey to France. Although the portmanteau held only two other gowns, both relics from Tante Marie's long-ago mourning for her husband, they were better than nothing.

Finally Annabelle decided to return to her brother's and spend the night there. He would be gone. Frederick would not return to London from the party at Budwell Abbey until Monday. Annabelle would sneak out with her portmanteau at dawn the following morning before anyone was stirring. On Saturday she would be leaving for the coast and should be in France by Sunday, twenty-four hours before her brother would return home and find that she had disappeared.

Back at her brother's, Annabelle pleaded weariness after her long journey from Yorkshire and requested that dinner be sent to her room. She retired immediately after it. As light was breaking over the eastern horizon the following morning, she crept

out of the house with her battered leather portmanteau and hurried the two blocks to the
Marquess's home in Berkeley Square.

When she reached Claire's apartment, she was
greeted with the news that Claire's mother had
rallied a little when she was told her daughter would
not be going to Paris.

'You see, it is all for the best that I go in your
place,' Annabelle said, not entirely confident that
she spoke the truth.

Later, over breakfast, Claire warned her not to
trust Rachel's abigail. 'I suspect she is in the pay
of Eustace Walford and is the conduit of his messages to Lady Rachel.'

'Does Rachel fancy herself wildly in love with
Walford?' Although Annabelle had no patience
with lovelorn young females bent upon disastrous
elopements, she knew how easily a handsome young
fortune-hunter determined to be charming could
captivate an inexperienced, impressionable girl not
yet out of the schoolroom into doing his bidding.

'Rachel does not confide in me, but she has not
the look of a girl in love,' Claire replied thoughtfully. 'Indeed, once her brother agreed to take her
to France, she seemed to lose all interest in
Walford.'

Perhaps the girl was not so gullible after all.
Annabelle sincerely hoped that this was the case.
She had no desire to have to frustrate an elopement.
Not that she doubted for a moment that she could
do so if Eustace Walford was at all like his silly,

vain eldest brother, who had been the most inept and foppish corkbrain she had ever met.

At nineteen, Eustace Walford, a dreamer who saw himself as a romantic Byronic hero, was an even vainer addlepate than Annabelle suspected. Nature's gifts to him had all been in the physical rather than the mental realm. He was very handsome, although not so handsome as he thought himself. No one could be. Tall and well proportioned, his fine form and chiselled face never failed to turn female heads.

He was already mired deep in dun territory with his creditors howling at him like a band of hungry wolves. He had no talent except for extravagant living and no income to support his expensive tastes. The only possible way that he could obtain the fortune he required was to marry it. Unfortunately, however, he suffered from a fatal impediment for a fortune-hunter: He had no desire to embrace the state of matrimony for many years yet.

Although he was in desperate financial shape, he was not desperate enough to marry. Instead, he was playing a rather deeper—and more dishonourable—game with Lady Rachel, one suggested by his brother Nugent's experience in eloping with Miss Glennell.

Lord Ellerton had made it clear to Rachel's aunt that he was determined not a breath of impropriety attach to his half-sister's name. Therefore, Eustace reasoned, the Marquess would pay royally to protect it. It was inconceivable to the callow youth that any

woman might find him less than utterly irresistible,
so he had not the slightest doubt that Rachel was
wildly in love with him. It would be easy to persuade her to elope with him to Gretna Green. Not
that he had any intention of reaching the border
with her. He would let her brother catch them well
before that and would pledge, for an exorbitant
price, his silence about the chit's scandalous
elopement with him.

His splendid scheme had suffered an unforeseen
check when Rachel had been unable to give her
governess the slip in recent days to meet him. So
he had had to content himself with impassioned
letters delivered to her by her abigail, Maud, whom
he paid well for her services as a go-between.

Too well, he thought bitterly as he approached
the street corner near Lord Ellerton's impressive
mansion, where he met the abigail each day. The
unscrupulous creature was positively mercenary in
her demands, and Eustace could ill afford the coins
she extracted from him.

To his irritation, Maud had not yet arrived, and
he was required to wait. Although he cut a far more
impressive figure than Annabelle's brother, he
favoured the same exaggerated fashions. The height
of his shirt points was the envy of every dandy in
London, and he was particularly proud of the in-
tricate folds of his white, heavily starched neckcloth, tied in a work of art known as the Oriental
that very few men or their valets could achieve.

The collection of fobs and seals that he wore on
his waistcoat was second to none, and all of his

coats fitted so exactly to his broad shoulders that he could not get in or out of them without the aid of a servant. As he waited for Maud, he proudly knew himself to be without a doubt the most bang-up blade in England.

A quarter-hour passed before Eustace saw Rachel's abigail hurrying towards him. She was an awkward bran-faced girl, only a few years older than her young mistress. To his enormous irritation, she brought no note from Lady Rachel in answer to the one that she had been paid to deliver the previous day. Today was the ninth day in a row that Rachel had not written to him.

This omission might have worried a more intelligent and less conceited man, but Eustace had allowed Maud to assure him that Rachel's new governess kept her under such close watch that she had been unable to sneak pen to paper.

In truth, Rachel had lost interest in Eustace once her brother had agreed to take her to France with him. The greedy Maud, however, had seen no point in telling Walford that, thereby endangering the steady supply of coins he paid her. She had also postponed telling him about the forthcoming trip to France because she had not been able to decide how she could use this information to extract the largest gain. Her position with Lady Rachel had, thus far, proved to be a disappointment. Maud had heard that the maids of certain young ladies had grown rich delivering secret messages from besotted admirers, but as yet her mistress was too young to have acquired such a retinue. In a couple of years perhaps... But Maud, like many avaricious persons, was impatient for quicker returns.

'What, no note again?' Eustace demanded. 'I cannot believe that one woman can keep Rachel under such close scrutiny she cannot manage to send me a few lines.'

Nor could Maud, and in an attempt to mollify him she said hastily, 'But now she has two governesses, and between them she is never alone.'

'Two! I never heard of such a thing. Why two?'

Unable to readily think of a convincing prevarication, Maud was forced to resort to the truth. 'The second is to accompany her to France.'

'Rachel goes to France?' Eustace demanded in alarm. 'When?'

'Tomorrow.'

Eustace was thunderstruck at the realisation that the large payment he had depended upon receiving from Lord Ellerton would drift away from him on the tide that carried Rachel to France. 'Why have you waited until now to tell me of this trip?'

Maud improvised hastily. 'Her brother only just decided that she must accompany him.'

'Surely Rachel cannot want to leave me!' he wailed in disbelief.

'Oh, no,' Maud assured him, seeing no possible gain for herself in telling him the truth. 'She is quite heartbroken at the prospect of leaving you, but she has no choice.'

Eustace demanded to know every detail of the proposed trip, but it took several minutes and a like number of coins to persuade Maud to divulge this information.

When he learned that the Marquess would not accompany his ward to the coast but would meet her at his yacht in Newhaven, Eustace conceived a splendid plan that appealed mightily to his romantic image of himself. It was inspired by a novel, a Gothic fantasy entitled *The Prisoner of Iago* that he had read to Rachel in his mellifluous voice, interspersing the author's passages with his own sly compliments. It was the story of a wicked uncle, Iago, who held his beautiful niece, Desdemona, a prisoner in his fortress in order to keep her inheritance for himself and prevent her from marrying her true love, Prince William.

One day when Iago was moving the heroine to another one of his castles, her brave young prince disguised himself as a masked bandit and, with pistols in hand, waylaid them on the road, snatching her from the evil clutches of her uncle. The heroine, overwhelmed with gratitude and love, fell into the prince's arms and they lived happily ever after.

Rachel had been much moved by the story, clearly identifying her half-brother with the wicked uncle and herself with Desdemona. Several times she had hinted to Eustace that, if only he would save her from her cruel half-brother, her gratitude would be as great as Desdemona's. Eustace was certain that he had only to re-enact this climactic scene, and Rachel, like Desdemona, would fall into his arms.

The only difference would be that he had no intention of living happily—or even unhappily—ever after with her.

Eustace would waylay the Earl's carriage when it was passing through an isolated wood on the road from London to Newhaven, force the coachman and the new governess from the vehicle, abandoning them in that remote area, while he continued on in it with Rachel and her abigail. For a moment Eustace's conscience pricked him for abandoning a helpless woman in such a remote spot, but this momentary twinge was quickly vanquished by the thought of the sum that Ellerton would pay him.

CHAPTER SIX

ANNABELLE, happily unaware of what lay ahead of her on the road to Newhaven, set out the following day with Rachel and her abigail in Lord Ellerton's coach, its ebony-black exterior with the Marquess's crest on the door polished to a high lustre.

His lordship had placed the three women in the charge of a stocky man with a seamed, leathery face who looked to be between fifty and sixty years. His name, Annabelle learned, was Putney, and the Marquess's other servants treated him with a deference that suggested he was a valued and influential employee of Ellerton's. When it came time for Putney to climb up on the riding seat, his slow awkwardness betrayed to Annabelle that the poor man suffered from painfully arthritic limbs which prevented him from moving with agility.

The coach left from Berkeley Square later than either Putney or Annabelle, very mindful of the Marquess's warning not to keep him waiting at Newhaven, would have liked. Rachel, whom her new governess gathered was chronically tardy, had delayed them. Not much, however, because her half-brother had warned her that if she were late, he would sail without her.

Now she was seated next to Annabelle, her lovely face framed by a charming straw hat decorated with a large midnight-blue bow that matched the colour of her stylish travelling dress. Beside her, Annabelle felt exceedingly dowdy in her old poke bonnet and Tante Marie's much altered black gown, the same one that she had worn travelling to London.

Maud, Rachel's abigail, sat opposite her mistress and the governess. The maid was exceedingly nervous. Her gaze never met Annabelle's but skittered guiltily away, making the new governess increasingly uneasy. Claire had been wise not to trust the girl.

Luxuriating in the comfort of the coach's thick burgundy cushions and squabs of cut velvet, Annabelle wryly contemplated how different this journey would be from the one she had completed only two days earlier on the roof of that dreadful stage. Fortune was indeed fickle.

Annabelle was determined to learn as much as she could about her new charge and, if possible, win her confidence. She was aided in this endeavour by Rachel's excitement over the prospect of seeing France. Annabelle capitalised on this by repeating some of the glowing tales of Paris that she had heard from her grand'mère, Tante Marie, and Jean-Louis.

'Have you been there?' Rachel asked, her curiosity overcoming her sullenness.

'No, but my grandmother, who was French, helped raise me.' Annabelle decided against mentioning Tante Marie, whose husband had died on the guillotine, and her son, Jean-Louis. She would have an awkward time explaining why an impoverished governess had an aunt who had married into the French nobility. It would be safer to say nothing about Marie and Jean-Louis, who had lived at Hillbrook for several years after fleeing France during the Terror. Tante Marie was dead now, and Jean-Louis, homesick for his native land, had returned to it after Napoleon crowned himself Emperor in 1804.

Annabelle stared out of the coach window. It was a rare day, warm and sunny with only one wispy white puff of a cloud in the distance to mar the unbroken blueness of the sky. They had reached Sussex and the rolling expanse of chalk downs with scattered woods and colourful fields of crested hairgrass, fescue, and meadow oatgrass quaking in the slight breeze. It was too late for the purple and gold splendour of the pasque flower, but several varieties of wild orchids were still in bloom, including the bee, the pyramidal, and the monkey, the latter with its petals that looked like miniature arms and legs.

A few minutes later they passed along a wood of evergreen yews, and Annabelle's attention was again drawn to Rachel's abigail. With each passing mile, the girl seemed to grow more nervous. Especially when they approached a wood. It is as though she is expecting something, Annabelle thought, her own unease growing.

'I have never seen so many yews all together,' Rachel observed.

'Yew woods are rare,' Annabelle told her. 'They grow only on chalk or limestone soil. Yew was prized in the Middle Ages because its wood was used to make the principal weapon of the time, the long-bow.'

'If yews were used to make weapons, why is it that they always grow in churchyards?'

Rachel's question pleased Annabelle. The girl clearly possessed both intelligence and curiosity. 'The yew was sacred in pagan times. Heathens may have planted them at their places of worship, and the Christians later used these sites for churches.'

'You are the first governess I have ever had who could answer my questions,' Rachel said approvingly.

Seeing that the girl's attitude had softened towards her at least temporarily, Annabelle set about with artful questions and observations to draw Rachel out and learn as much as she could. Soon the girl was chattering with surprising animation, proving herself to be a far livelier and more engaging young lady than her new governess had initially suspected.

Furthermore, Annabelle's subtle but astute interrogation exposed a picture of Rachel's life that did much to explain her behaviour. By nature, the girl was very different from the unpleasant first impression Annabelle had had of her. True, she was spoiled, but her sullenness and defiance sprang not from a morose or disagreeable temperament, but from unhappiness, loneliness, and a lively terror of her half-brother. The principal blame for this fear lay not with him, but with Rachel's late mama.

The girl would have been startled, even shocked, if she had had any idea how much she was revealing, quite unconsciously, to Annabelle about her own and her mother's characters.

Rachel had not been many years out of leading strings when her father had died. Her mother had been delighted to retire to the dowager house at Elmdale, where she had embraced the life of an invalid recluse. Which would have been fine and good, had she not had a young daughter to raise, Annabelle thought irately. Instead of attending to her child's needs, Lady Ellerton had spent her days lying upon her chaise-longue.

Her stepson must also have noted her deficiencies as a mother, for she had lived in constant terror that he would remove her only child from her custody. As Rachel's legal guardian, it had been his right to do so, and it might have been happier for the girl if he had. The dower house had been a lonely, isolated prison for Rachel until her mother's death. Despite the dowager's fears, however, Ellerton had acceded to her wishes in any matter concerning her daughter's upbringing.

Whenever he had politely invited the Marchioness to visit him or called upon her, she had taken refuge in her bed, sending word that she was far too ill to see him. The woman's obvious fear of her stepson had infected her daughter, and whenever Rachel had disobeyed, her mother had threatened to send her to live with her brother, who would inflict all sorts of dire but unnamed tortures on her. Furthermore, when the time came, he would, just as her ladyship's own father had done to her, marry his half-sister off without so much as consulting her to an ugly old man who would treat her wretchedly.

In short, Rachel had been raised by her mother to regard her half-brother as an inhuman ogre. Since Lady Ellerton had been determined to keep her daughter as well as herself out of the new Marquess's sight, there had been no personal contact between them that might have dispelled Rachel's terrifying impression of him.

As the girl had grown older, her mother had sought to curb her spirit by hiring governesses selected for their sternness rather than for their accomplishments. They had been, without exception, cold, stiff, disapproving, straitlaced martinets. Their chief aim had not been to impart knowledge and understanding to their charge but to impose their will upon her obstinate one.

Not surprisingly, Rachel, spirited child that she was, had learned to give as well as she got. Nevertheless, Annabelle's sympathy lay with the poor girl, whose education had been dry lessons learned by rote. It made Annabelle realise how lucky she herself had been to have had dear Claire. Rachel was a bright child, but no attempt had been made to awaken her mind, and Annabelle was determined to remedy that.

When Rachel related the tyranny of one particularly offensive woman, Annabelle said warmly, 'No wonder you detest governesses. I should have made her an apple-pie bed.'

'I did!' Rachel exclaimed gleefully, momentarily forgetting that she was talking to another member of that hated fraternity. Remembering, she clapped her hand over her mouth.

But Annabelle said warmly, 'Good for you.'

The girl's dark eyes widened into full moons at this unexpected answer. In a voice fraught with suspicion, she said, 'But you are a governess, too.'

'Yes, and if I ever acted towards you the way that woman did, you would be quite justified in making me an apple-pie bed, too.' Annabelle's eyes sparkled mischievously. 'And if you treat me badly, perhaps I will do the same to you.'

'I think I like you after all,' Rachel said. 'You are the only governess I have ever had that I could talk to.'

Between Rachel's mother and those wretched women she had employed, Annabelle was amazed that the girl had retained as much spirit as she had.

After the dreadfully boring, restricted life that Rachel had led at Elmdale, it was no wonder that she had been enchanted by her aunt's boisterous, ramshackle household, always brimming over with visitors. It had given Rachel her first taste of the carefree society of other young people. With four unmarried daughters of only passing prettiness and meagre portions to be got rid of, Aunt Bess had filled her house at every opportunity with young bachelors. Rachel, having the advantage of both beauty and a handsome fortune, had been a great success among them. She had delighted in this attention after the quiet isolation of the dowager house. In short, she had had the time of her young life.

Annabelle realised with amusement that Rachel had been inclined while at her aunt's to fall in and out of love with some frequency. Her infatuation with Eustace Walford had consisted mostly of an admiration for the stirring way that he had read *The Prisoner of Iago* to her. Young Eustace apparently had a talent for histrionics. The book, however, had come to an end, and so had Rachel's interest in its reader.

'But you threatened to elope with him,' Annabelle reminded her.

'I had no intention of doing so,' the girl admitted candidly.

She went on to tell Annabelle how furious she had been when her half-brother had removed her from her aunt, thereby proving that he truly was the cruel monster her mother had always insisted he was. Still very much frightened of him, the girl had retreated behind a façade of sullen contrariness that must have sorely tested his temper.

Annabelle found herself sympathising with both of them. She was determined to find a way to bring brother and sister to a better understanding of each other.

Looking out of the window, Annabelle saw the road ahead disappeared into the dark depths of a dense forest. She was impatient to reach the coast. It occurred to her that she was eagerly looking forward to seeing Lord Ellerton again, and this realisation shocked her. She was too old and too wise to have her heart fluttering over a man, particularly the Notorious Marquess.

The carriage, travelling at a rapid pace, entered the shade of the forest, and soon the vehicle's interior grew appreciably darker and cooler. Relishing the sudden change in temperature, Annabelle rested her head against the velvet squab and closed her eyes.

A sudden commotion shattered the silence of the quiet wood. There was a shouting and then, very near the coach, the unmistakable bark of a gun.

CHAPTER SEVEN

EUSTACE WALFORD had chosen to waylay Lord
Ellerton's coach at a spot where the road from
London to Newhaven wound through a forest of
oak and beech and hazel trees. He concealed
himself beyond a sharp curve that would require a
fast-moving coach to slow. When the Marquess's
carriage rounded this bend, Eustace, masked and
armed with a pistol in each hand, would emerge
and force it to stop. He had spent some time the
previous night practising to make his normally
mellifluous voice sound gruff and menacing.

As he waited beside the road, edged with bracken
and heather, he was well pleased with himself. His
appearance, on which he had lavished considerably
greater attention than on his abduction plan,
pleased him even more. He looked so fine that when
he had finished dressing that morning he had spent
several awestruck minutes before a long mirror in
his rooms admiring himself. Never had there been
a more dashing highwayman, he had thought, as
he had tried on his mask, a very grand affair of
black satin studded with brilliants around the eye-
holes that he had acquired for a masquerade.

Eager to overwhelm Lady Rachel not only with
his bold courage in rescuing her from her evil
brother but also with his exquisite taste, he had

worn his newest coat, an extravagant affair of turquoise velvet that he fancied flattered his fair complexion and blue-green eyes. It was decorated with large gold buttons and worn over a satin waistcoat boasting broad turquoise and gold stripes. Never mind that both garments had been intended for night-time galas in London rather than daylight abductions in the woods.

Eustace had eschewed buckskin riding breeches as too prosaic for his coat. Instead, he had chosen, impractical as they were for the saddle, a pair of white silk pantaloons.

Since it was a matter of enormous pride to him that he wore the highest, stiffest shirt points and cravat in London, it would never have occurred to him to leave them off today of all days. In fact, the better part of an hour had been spent in the arrangement and tying of his neckcloth.

To protect his finery from the dust of the road and to give himself a more sinister appearance to the Marquess's coachman, Eustace had enveloped himself in the voluminous folds of a black velvet cloak that he had worn to the same masquerade for which he had acquired his mask.

In choosing to use the cloak for his début as a highwayman, however, he had failed to calculate how hot the day would be. Eustace had not been long upon the road to Newhaven before he was forced to remove it, revealing the splendour of his raiment to several astonished farmers driving their carts, piled high with produce, along the road towards London.

He wished he could shed his velvet coat as well, but unfortunately it fitted with such precision that he could not get in and out of it without assistance.

As the heat of the day climbed, so did both his temper and his discomfort. He was, at best, an indifferent rider. The precarious state of his family's finances had precluded a country estate where he would have spent part of his boyhood in the saddle. Instead, he had been raised in London, and only occasionally had his father had the blunt to pay for riding lessons on a broken-down horse from a cheap stable.

Although Eustace's understanding was decidedly inferior, he was sufficiently up to the mark to realise that no man mounted on the kind of nag he normally rode would cut a very dashing figure as he abducted his Desdemona. So he had chosen a showy, spirited chestnut that he soon learned had various annoying habits, including ignoring Eustace's hand upon the reins and assuming his own pace, which his inexperienced rider found unnerving.

Eustace knew even less about guns than horses. Firearms made him exceedingly nervous, and he had never fired one in his life. But he had recognised that he would need a brace of pistols if he was to force Ellerton's coach to stop. So he had acquired a pair from a pawn shop that he frequented. Knowing nothing about guns, he had picked them for their intimidating size rather than for their quality. He assumed them to be unloaded and was happy to leave them that way, for he did not like above half the idea of carrying loaded pistols upon his person. Nor would he need to fire them. Their size, coupled with his mask and his intimidating voice, would bring the Marquess's coachman to an instant halt.

Eustace had calculated his departure from London so that he would arrive at the bend in the road where he planned to execute the abduction about a quarter hour before Ellerton's coach. Reaching the spot, he extracted his glittering mask and the guns from his saddlebag. The pistols were so large they were dashed cumbersome to hold, especially when he had also to control his troublesome mount.

As he waited impatiently for Ellerton's coach, he envisaged how ecstatic Rachel would be when she recognised her hero, which she would do instantly despite his mask. His sartorial splendour would leave no doubt in her mind as to his identity and, like Desdemona in *The Prisoner of Iago*, she would fall adoringly on his neck, awed by his courage and full of gratitude for rescuing her from her evil half-brother.

The new governess would be a problem, Eustace thought with a frown. Maud had said the woman was a skinny spinster. Undoubtedly, she would dissolve into strong hysterics. He disliked the din that she would raise, but it could not be helped, and there was not a soul within miles to hear her. Perhaps, he thought hopefully, the woman would faint from fright and remain unconscious until he had carried Rachel and her abigail off in the Marquess's coach.

The governess and the coachman would be stranded until another carriage happened along, and that might be a very long time. There had not been another vehicle on the road for the past hour. What if none passed, and the pair was forced to spend the night in the woods? That might be for the best, Eustace decided, since it would give him more time to flee with Rachel.

He would tell her that he was taking her to Gretna Green but would go instead to a remote inn, favoured by men of the *ton* for licentious frolics. The landlord knew better than to ask questions of his well-paying guests. Instead, he pocketed the outrageous sum he charged for his rooms, and turned a blind eye and deaf ear to the scandalous scenes beneath his roof.

Eustace, well pleased by his ingenuity, thought greedily of the sum that he would demand from the Marquess for his silence about Lady Rachel's shocking indiscretion. This amount had risen sharply since the previous day. There was, after all, the expense of his horse, the pistols, and the exorbitant inn.

A possibility, previously unconsidered, suddenly caused Eustace's palms to grow sweaty around the pistols. What if, instead of paying him off, the Marquess called him out? Although duelling was no longer in fashion, Ellerton, in his youth, a score of years ago, had had a notable career on the field of honour. His skill with both sword and pistols was widely held to be unequalled.

Eustace's courage threatened to fail him until he reminded himself that the Marquess would want absolute silence about this affair. Were he to call Eustace out, it would be the talk of the *ton* within hours.

He heard Ellerton's coach approaching at a sedate pace on the other side of the bend. Eustace was so eager to launch his attack he entered into the road even before the horses came into view. He aimed his pistols at the coachman on the box of the huge old-fashioned travelling carriage as it lumbered around the curve at a snail's pace. Eustace was startled that the Marquess would use such an outmoded, uncomfortable vehicle, but he did not refine upon this detail.

'Halt or I will shoot,' he yelled in the gruff, threatening voice he had practised the previous night.

The elderly coachman, who looked very nearly as ancient as the vehicle he was driving, instantly complied.

To the occupants of the coach Eustace shouted, 'Open that door or I'll fire.'

His order was obeyed with such alacrity and violence that the door crashed against the side of the coach.

It was then that Eustace discovered that, no matter how impressive the most stiffly starched cravat and highest collar points were among London dandies, they were a severe handicap to a highwayman, presenting an insurmountable obstacle to his inspecting the victims within the coach while still astride his horse.

No contortion that he could think of would permit him to see inside the carriage while the starched straitjacket round his neck locked his head at an upward angle. Nor did he think he could manage, what with his huge pistols and uncooperative horse, to dismount very gracefully.

In frustration he tore at the exquisite neckcloth that had been so patiently and painstakingly tied that morning, leaving it hanging messily around his neck, and ripped open his collar. Freed of these restraints, he looked down at the coach's occupants.

Two pairs of bulging, terrified female eyes were staring at him. One belonged to an elderly crone, whose plain, dark clothes indicated her to be a maid.

On the seat opposite her sat her mistress, a white-haired dowager as fat as she was old, dressed in an elaborate travelling costume and clutching to her enormous breast a large jewel case in tooled leather.

So stupefied was Eustace by the discovery that he had stopped the wrong coach, he could only stare at the two women, his large pistols still aimed at them, wondering what the blazes he was to do now.

When he made no attempt to dismount, the dowager, blathering incoherently, held the jewel case out for him to take. Thinking of the sad state of his finances and the rich, pawnable gems it would contain, he was fleetingly tempted to take it, but then rejected the idea. His understanding was far from acute, but he was not such a crackbrain that he failed to realise such a robbery could lead to unpleasant consequences for him—like Newgate or even the gallows.

He gestured impatiently at the old lady to keep her case and at her coachman to move on, but neither seemed able to comprehend his wishes. The coachman remained frozen in fright on his box, and the dowager thrust the case at her maid, who jumped out of the coach and tried to hand it up to Eustace on his horse.

When he failed to take the case from her, it fell from her terrified fingers, crashing so violently to the ground that its clasp popped and some of the contents spilled out. Any interest Eustace might have had in the case immediately evaporated. All but a few pieces were the most trumpery pieces of paste he had ever seen, and the few genuine ones were not of a quality worth hanging for.

This realisation coupled with the sound of another vehicle approaching propelled Eustace out of his saddle. Jamming the pistols awkwardly in his belt, he jumped down, desperate to be rid of the dowager and her coach.

He snarled at the maid to get back in the vehicle. As she obeyed, he kneeled down, hastily scooped up the jewels from the chalky earth along with a liberal supply of dirt, and dumped them back into the case. He shoved the case at the dowager.

But she refused to take it, and it very nearly tumbled to the ground again.

The sound of the second coach was very close now. In a panic Eustace threw the jewel case on the floor of the carriage and slammed the door. Pulling his big pistols from his belt, he waved them wildly at the ancient coachman, shouting at him to be off.

It was, however, beyond the astonished old man's comprehension why a highwayman would go to all the trouble of holding up a carriage and then order it away without taking anything. More precious time was required to make Eustace's wishes perfectly understood.

By then the neophyte highwayman had no chance to retie his cravat hanging untidily around his neck, or to remount his horse, nor even to put on his dashing black velvet cloak before the coach rounded the bend.

Eustace was only vaguely conscious that he might no longer cut quite as fine a figure as he had when he had set out that morning. Sweat stained the turquoise underarms of his beautiful velvet coat and trickled down his face from beneath his mask. His collar points were sadly drooping. The knees of his white silk pantaloons were dirty from kneeling on the ground to restore the dowager's jewels to her case, and he was hampered from brushing at the spots by the big awkward pistols in his hands.

The second carriage had had to slow drastically for the curve, and Eustace pointed his brace of pistols at the man on the box, ordering him to stop or he would shoot.

To Eustace's surprise, this command seemed to have no effect. Instead of halting, the coachman, holding the reins in one hand, urged his team forward while reaching towards a holster beside him with his other. At that moment Eustace's nervous mount jostled his arm, and his hand tightened around the gun.

A shot rang out, wood splintered, and the holster the driver had been reaching for, as well as the gun it contained, crashed to the ground. The coachman, tardily divining the seriousness of his assailant's intent, stopped the carriage.

It was hard to say who was more shocked, the man on the box who was staring at the hand he had come within a fraction of an inch of having blown away or Eustace, who belatedly realised that his pistols were loaded. *Loaded.* He turned as pale as the chalky earth beneath his feet as he recalled how carelessly he had stuffed them into his belt.

It was a moment before he could recover himself sufficiently to order the coachman to keep his hands high in the air, and even then his tone was not as steady as he would have liked it to have been. But the man, eyeing the unfired pistol in his assailant's other hand, complied.

Eustace turned his attention to the passengers inside the coach, ordering them out in the gruff, threatening voice he had rehearsed.

Through the closed door he heard a woman's quiet voice, so calm he envied her, say, 'Do not open the door.'

He grabbed the handle and flung the door open himself. Inside, Rachel was seated beside her governess, a thin female in an ugly black dress and austere poke bonnet. Maud was seated opposite them. Eustace steeled himself for the governess's certain hysteria at the sight of a masked bandit. To his astonishment, however, her eyes seemed to light up with laughter as she examined him. What the blazes could she find so funny? Eustace wondered, oblivious to how unique his costume was in the annals of highway banditry. Was the woman mad? Yes, of course, that was it. Fear had unhinged her.

Rachel's reaction was equally surprising to him. Instead of flinging herself on his neck, she stared at him with terror-glazed eyes. He had expected her to recognise him instantly from his sartorial splendour. He could not conceive how she could possibly have failed to do so.

But he had no time to ponder this, for she began to shriek at the top of her amazingly strong lungs. He would never have thought that such a tiny little thing could make so much noise, and he was wondering miserably how he was going to get her to stop, when the governess solved his dilemma by telling the girl in a voice of steel to stop acting like a ninnyhammer.

Rachel was so taken aback by this admonishment that she paused in mid-scream, and the governess told Eustace in the most odiously condescending voice, 'Do be careful how you point those pistols, my dear boy. You clearly do not have the slightest notion of how to handle them.'

Since there was more truth in her statement than he liked to admit, it raised his hackles. 'You'll see how well I can fire them if you don't get out of there this minute,' he blustered, pointing the pistols at her.

He expected her to cower in terror, but instead she warned kindly, 'Take care that you don't shoot yourself in the foot. Or some even more vital part.'

His hands trembled a little at the warning. Recovering himself, he waved the heavy pistols at her to emphasise the seriousness of his intent. 'I said get out!'

But the governess only looked at him without moving, her eyes still alight with amusement, as if this were all some sort of joke. Well, he'd quickly disabuse her of that notion. 'Get out or I will shoot you!'

Still, the infuriating governess did not move. Instead, she said calmly, 'I have no intention of getting out.'

'What?' he asked, forgetting his gruff voice. The pistols wavered nervously in his hands.

'I said I have no intention of getting out of this coach,' she repeated, clearly enunciating her words as though she were speaking to a sapskull.

He made his voice as menacing as he could. 'If you do not get out this instant, I will shoot you.'

The governess stared unperturbed at the pistols levelled at her and said calmly, 'Then shoot.'

Eustace could not believe his ears. 'What did you say?' he stammered, his voice rising an octave higher than normal.

'I said shoot me.'

Nonplussed, Eustace could only stare at her. He had not the smallest notion of what to do now.

'I must warn you, however,' the governess continued in that maddeningly cool voice of hers, 'that shooting a helpless woman is certain to send you to the gallows.'

A vision of himself dangling from a noose flashed through his mind, and he shuddered.

'So stop making such a cake of yourself, Eustace Walford, and let us be on our way,' the governess said. 'Or we will miss the afternoon tide.'

He stared in amazement at the woman, whom he was certain he had never laid eyes on before in his life. 'How do you know who I am,' he stammered.

'You favour your eldest brother. Although I fear that you are even more inept than he.'

'So it is you, Eustace,' Rachel cried angrily.

He nodded, confidently expecting a suitable expression of her gratitude for his efforts on her behalf.

But she did not look in the least grateful. Nor sound it either. 'What do you mean by scaring me to death?' she demanded.

'I...I am rescuing you from your terrible brother,' he stammered, 'from your evil Iago, my beloved Desdemona.'

'I don't want to be rescued,' she said crossly.

'But...but,' he floundered, 'but of...of course you do. We will elope to Gretna Green.'

Her lovely little face wrinkled in disgust. 'I don't want to go to Gretna Green. I have my heart set on going to France. Why would anyone wish to go to Scotland instead of France?'

'But we can be married in Gretna Green,' he pleaded.

'I prefer France.'

'Then I'll take you to France,' he said desperately.

'How?' she demanded succinctly. 'Do you have a yacht?'

'No, but...'

'My brother does, and I prefer to go to France with him and with Anna.'

It had never before occurred to Eustace that Rachel or any other woman might fail to find him irresistible, and he stared at her as though she had taken leave of her senses.

'How did you even know that I was going to Paris?' Rachel demanded petulantly.

The governess looked suddenly interested. 'Have you not been in communication with him, Rachel?'

'Not since Jason agreed to take me to France.'

'But you know that I have written to you every day!' he cried.

'What an odious untruth,' Rachel retorted indignantly. 'I have heard nothing from you. I would never go anywhere with such a liar!'

Remembering how desperately under the hatches he was, Eustace reached into the coach to grab her arm and haul her out. 'You will come with me!' he yelled furiously.

Rachel sank back into the cushions in fear, but the governess slapped Eustace's arm away before he could touch the girl.

'It is one thing to persuade a young lady to elope willingly with you,' the governess said calmly. 'It is quite another to forcibly drag her from a carriage and kidnap her at gunpoint. I can assure you that the Bow Street runners will be much quicker than your creditors to run you to ground, and it will be the gallows for certain.'

By now sweat was pouring down Eustace's face, plastering his clothes to his body. He knew that the woman spoke the truth.

'If you do not wish to dance upon nothing,' the governess continued in that odiously unperturbed voice of hers, 'return to London and let us continue our journey unmolested. If you do so, perhaps I may be able to persuade Lord Ellerton not to enrol you in Whittington's college.'

This reference to Newgate Prison rendered Eustace speechless and ashen-faced beneath his black satin mask.

The governess leaned out of the door and called to the coachman, watching in such fascination that he had forgotten to keep his hands up, 'Drive on, Putney.'

The coach surged forward, leaving Eustace behind in its dust, staring after it.

CHAPTER EIGHT

LORD ELLERTON angrily paced the quay at Newhaven, oblivious to the strong smell of the sea and to all else except the falling tide and passing time. His carriage with Rachel and her new governess should have arrived nearly an hour ago. If they did not come soon, they would miss the afternoon tide.

Where the deuce could they be? Their tardiness could not be Putney's fault, for the Marquess knew that his loyal retainer would not fail him if he could help it. It would have come as a great surprise—and insult—to Ellerton's affronted peers that he often preferred the company of Putney, who over the years had become as much friend and confidant as servant, to theirs. Putney had a tart, blunt tongue that was cherished by his master, who was always quite willing to take as good as he gave.

Despite Rachel's dislike for rising before noon, the Marquess did not think her responsible for the delay. He had firmly impressed upon her that he would sail without her should she be late, and he was certain that for once in her life she would be punctual. That left only the new governess to blame, and Ellerton was quite willing to do so.

In the two days since he had agreed to employ her, he had been much plagued by thoughts of Miss

Anna Smith. Indeed, he had given her more thought than he had any woman, including his lovely incognitas, in years. As he had ridden from Dorset to Newhaven that morning, he had been astounded by how much he was looking forward to seeing that thin, plain creature again and to more verbal sparring with her. So disconcerted had he been by this discovery that since then he had been determined to find whatever fault he could with her. Now he was perfectly willing to convict her of responsibility for the coach being late without a shred of evidence against her. What a dressing down he would give her when he saw her.

Not that it looked as if he would have the opportunity to do so very soon. He stared with baleful eyes at the receding tide, wondering if her clearly delicate constitution had become overwrought by the journey and Putney had been forced to stop at a wayside inn until she revived. This possibility further fuelled Ellerton's temper, for he had no sympathy with the complaints of vaporish female travellers.

While Anna indulged herself in her megrims, his yacht, *The Sea Princess*, lay at the ready in the nearly deserted tidal harbour formed by the mouth of the Ouse River. The other outgoing boats had already been carried on the tide past the small fort that guarded the harbour's narrow entrance into the open waters of the English Channel.

The wagon containing his party's baggage for the trip had arrived the previous night. Everything had been stowed aboard *The Sea Princess* hours ago, although there had been some delay while Mrs Potter's pieces had been separated out to be returned to London. Did a woman exist who did not insist on travelling with a small mountain of baggage? he wondered waspishly. Undoubtedly Anna's would further delay their departure.

Irritably pacing the quay, he cast a discerning eye at the sea, and did not like what he saw. Dark, forbidding clouds were moving across the water towards him. Beyond the harbour the waves were increasing in size, and grey water was roiling with whitecaps. A storm was blowing up, and it would be a rough crossing. If Anna had been undone by the journey from London, what would the channel in a storm do to her? She was certain to be deathly sick the entire trip.

He was shaken from these unhappy thoughts by the clang of galloping hooves and iron wheels on cobblestones. He turned from his worried contemplation of the channel to see his carriage, its usually gleaming ebony finish dulled by a heavy coating of dust, rushing towards him.

As it stopped beside him, he shouted at Putney not to climb down from the box but to take the carriage on to the stable as soon as the women had left it.

'My lord, I beg a word with you,' Putney said.

'Not now! There's no time,' the Marquess said, throwing open the coach door. 'We will miss the tide. Be aboard the boat in ten minutes.'

The usually sullen, rebellious Rachel, looking more subdued and shaken than her brother had ever seen her, stepped down from the carriage.

'Why the deuce are you so late in getting here?' he demanded irritably.

Rachel's face whitened. 'It was not my fault, Jason. Truly it was not. Was it, Anna?'

'No, it was not,' her fascinating smoky voice concurred from within the carriage, earning a look of sincere gratitude from her charge.

Anna stepped out, carrying a battered leather portmanteau. She was again clad in that outmoded black gown she had worn when he had interviewed her, and her hair was hidden under the same un-flattering black poke bonnet. Why the deuce didn't she make an effort to dress better? he wondered, irrationally venting his irritation on her clothes. He was certain that she would be far more attractive if only she made a little effort.

'Don't you have a more flattering gown than this one?' he demanded.

'How complimentary you are, my lord,' she said calmly.

Once the words were out of Jason's mouth, he could not believe that he had been so churlish as to speak them. To cover his embarrassment, he said sharply, 'It is not my nature to be complimentary!'

'No,' she agreed pleasantly, 'only to be insulting and disagreeable.'

Rachel's maid emerged from the coach, the Marquess slammed the door, and the vehicle clattered away as Putney hastened to carry out his master's order.

Jason turned to Anna, eyeing her shabby, solitary portmanteau. 'Where is the rest of your baggage?'

'This is all that I have.'

Jason instantly gave voice to his incredulity. 'But we will be gone for months.'

Her lips tightened, and two bright red spots burned in her cheeks, but she only said softly, 'Yes, I know.'

He belatedly realised that he was seeing the sum total of her possessions, and he despised himself for having been so ungentlemanly as to call attention to her poverty. To apologise now in front of Rachel would only draw further attention to it and shame her still further. His irritation with himself spilled over into his voice as he demanded testily, 'Why have you kept me waiting?'

A martial light sparkled in Anna's eyes, but she said in the sweetest and most conciliatory of tones, 'Naturally, I did so on purpose, expressly because you warned me so emphatically not to.'

He had deserved that, he thought appreciatively. 'I ought to send you packing back to London,' he told her, his rough tone negated by the amusement in his eyes.

But Rachel thought him serious, and she cried, 'Oh, no, Jason! Please do not send Anna away. She is the only governess that I have ever liked.'

Jason, remembering the warfare between Rachel and every one of a long succession of governesses, was astonished that Anna had managed to win over the chit in less than two days, when every other woman, even Mrs Potter, had failed.

'Collect your abigail and go aboard my boat,' he told his sister, wanting to apologise privately to Anna before they boarded *The Sea Princess*. 'I wish to be private with Miss Smith.'

'Please let Anna come with us, Jason,' pleaded Rachel, not moving a step.

'I will leave you both behind if you do not immediately obey me,' he said sternly, knowing that this threat would put a quick end to the discussion.

Rachel cast him one last beseeching look before beckoning to her maid to accompany her.

As the pair moved towards his yacht, Jason said quietly to Anna, 'Please forgive me for embarrassing you a minute ago. I did not do so intentionally. I have an abominably quick tongue, and I was angry because you were late. It did not immediately occur to me that you might not have many other clothes.'

She rewarded him with a smile that seemed to warm him like a fire on a winter day. 'You are forgiven,' she said in that smoky voice that was as warm as her smile. 'While Lady Rachel is out of hearing, I must advise you to cast off her abigail. She has been accepting bribes from Eustace Walford to carry his love letters to her mistress.'

Jason shrugged indifferently. 'He is wasting his blunt. Rachel is not in love with him and has no intention of eloping with him.'

'Unfortunately, Eustace did not perfectly understand that.'

'What?' Jason asked in surprise. 'Do you know him?'

'We met today upon the road from London.'

'The road from London? What the deuce was he doing there?'

'He was enacting a scene from *The Prisoner of Iago*, under the mistaken impression that Lady Rachel, his "Fair Desdemona", wished to run away to Gretna Green with him.'

'I imagine that she set him straight quick enough,' Jason said complacently. 'Rachel threatened to elope with him only to get me to take her to France.'

Anna gave him an odd look. 'And her tactic worked.'

Something slightly censorious in Anna's blue eyes and in that marvellous voice of hers suddenly made Jason feel strangely in need of justifying himself. 'Yes, it did,' he admitted defensively. 'Unfortunately, Rachel is such a spoiled, contrary chit, so used to having her own way, that I feared she might run away with Walford out of spite if I left her behind. I could not chance that happening. Before his death my father made me vow that I would see her well and happily married, and I will not fail him this time.' Jason thought bitterly of that other time he had failed him. 'I will not have a breath of scandal attached to her name.'

'And certainly you are an expert on scandal,' Anna said provocatively, but he did not rise to the bait. 'Get rid of the abigail at once,' she urged. 'Rachel will certainly meet some charming young men who are considerably more irresistible than that silly fop Walford. And you would not want her maid aiding them as she did with Walford.'

Jason knew that Anna was right, but he could not suppress an audible sigh at the thought of the scene that this would precipitate. He had been suspicious of the maid from the start and would have sacked her before now had not Rachel professed to like her excessively. Furthermore, the maid would be righteously indignant at being turned out so abruptly.

When he explained this to Anna, she only laughed. 'At the moment I wager that there is nothing Maud wishes for so much as to escape your yacht.'

The governess gestured towards the abigail, who was standing on the quay, rigid with fear, as she looked at the boiling sea beyond the harbour. Her face was already green.

Good God, Jason wondered in dismay, was he to be burdened with three sick females on the crossing?

'Offer her a month's salary and a ticket back to London,' Anna advised, 'and I predict she will be delighted. As for Rachel, you will have no difficulty with her if you but give her a critical perusal, like the one you gave me the other day. Then tell her that she looks too dowdy for Paris and you fear that her maid may be to blame. Promise to hire her a French maid who will be up to the mark on all the latest Paris fashions.'

Jason regarded the governess with new respect. Rachel would instantly swallow the bait. Clearly Anna knew how to handle his difficult sister to a nicety.

'I will help Rachel dress until a maid can be hired,' Anna offered. 'Now, should we not be sailing? The tide has dropped several inches even while we have been talking.'

It dropped an additional two feet before *The Sea Princess* was under way. First, Maud had to be dealt with. As Anna had predicted, Rachel had been so excited at the thought of a French maid that she made no objection to leaving Maud behind. That female, who had been rendered ill by the mere sight of the crashing waves, had been delighted to remain on dry land.

At last the outgoing tide carried *The Sea Princess* into the grey waters of the Channel. Anna, who was standing with Jason and Rachel at the rail, observed, 'What a fine tidal harbour this is.'

'Yes, one of the best between Dover and the Isle of Wight,' Jason agreed. 'Boats can be carried as far as twenty miles up the river if they catch the tide right.'

'Why is it called Newhaven?' Rachel asked.

'The Ouse used to flow into the ocean at Seaford,' Jason said. 'But storms in the sixteenth century blocked the outlet and a new channel was formed near here. To prevent flooding, a cut was made to the sea, providing a new harbour and giving boats a new haven.'

Once past the fort that guarded the haven's entrance, the progress of *The Sea Princess* became very much rougher. The sky was darkly ominous, and the yacht pitched and heaved on the angry waves.

Jason looked apprehensively at Anna for signs of queasiness. She was certain to be desperately sick very soon, and she looked so exceedingly fragile. But, to his surprise, she seemed to take no notice of the upheaval beneath her feet. Instead, she was staring back at the rolling green hills of England and the high chalk cliffs, their tops carpeted with green, that traced the coast.

'Homesick already?' he asked, mockingly.

'No, only admiring the view. In truth, I am happy to be leaving. I am eager to see France.'

'You will be even more eager by the time we get there,' Jason predicted. 'It promises to be a rough crossing. I fear you will be quite ill.'

'Nonsense,' she said vigorously. 'I don't get seasick.'

Her certainty amused him. 'That is what most people think before they have been to sea,' he told her, sure that before many more minutes her cool composure would vanish.

But, as it turned out, his concern should have been reserved for his sister. Rachel quickly became so ill that she disappeared into her cabin, declaring that she preferred to die in a horizontal position upon her bed rather than hanging over the railing.

The sea was proving to be so violent that even Jason, who normally never suffered a moment's uneasiness aboard ship, was feeling queasy. He was much relieved when Anna, still showing not the least sign of distress, volunteered to care for Rachel.

Shortly after the women went below, Jason was joined at the rail by Putney, who gave his employer an account of what had happened upon the road from London.

'Walford shot at you!' the astonished Marquess exclaimed.

'Nearly blew my hand away, but it was only a lucky shot. I think he was as surprised by it as meself.'

Jason, wondering why Anna had not told him the details of the meeting with Walford, asked, 'How did you thwart him?'

''Twasn't me, but the go'erness,' Putney told him, more than willing to give credit where it was due. 'Right splendid, she was.'

When he finished relating the details of what had happened, Jason was torn between amazement that a woman had displayed the courage that Anna had and deep regret that he had missed the confrontation between the redoubtable governess and Walford. Heretofore, his admiration of a woman had been confined to her beauty and her skill at pleasing him, but now he was increasingly fascinated by Miss Anna Smith, even though her appearance was as plain and dowdy as her name. He had never met another woman like her. 'She is amazing,' he murmured aloud.

'Aye, that she is,' agreed Putney, who normally had as little use for women as his master. 'Looks so fragile that a flea would scare her, but she never turned a hair when that young fool pointed them pistols at her. She's got bottom, that one does. A real gem, you've found there. She'll be just the ticket for Lady Rachel.'

CHAPTER NINE

WHEN Annabelle awoke the following morning in the small cabin she shared with Rachel, sunshine was streaming through the tiny circle of the porthole. The sea was so calm beneath her that she was certain the yacht must be in the lee of land.

Jumping up from her berth, she hurried to look out of the porthole. She blinked at how bright it was outside, surprised that the sun was already so high in the sky. Land lay ahead, but her view of it was narrowly circumscribed by the small size of the porthole. All that she could make out were chalk cliffs with alternating layers of flint and yellow marl. Then, far in the distance, she caught a glimpse of massive fortification. Annabelle surmised that she was seeing the Alabaster Coast of France.

Having yearned for so long to visit the land of her grand'mère and of Jean-Louis, she had to stifle her impulse to dash up on deck for a better view. She could not leave Rachel. During the worst of the storm last night, the girl had made her new governess swear that she would remain at her side until they reached land—if they ever did. Annabelle had made enormous progress in winning the girl's liking and trust, and this would be undermined if Rachel were to awake and find her gone.

Turning from the porthole, Annabelle gazed down at the girl, lying on one of the two berths that, between them, nearly filled the cabin. The storm had tossed the boat about like a toy, and Rachel had been as frightened and as seasick as anyone Annabelle had ever seen. She had comforted the girl and had done her best to reassure her that, fierce as the storm was, the boat would not be swallowed up by the sea. Although severe, the storm had not been nearly so bad as the hurricane that Annabelle had survived on her return from Barbados. But to Rachel, this introduction to the sea had been terrifying. The poor child had clung to her governess as though she were her lifeline.

At the storm's zenith, Jason had knocked on the cabin door. Rachel had been in the noisy throes of her sea-induced misery. Annabelle, leaving her with her basin, opened the door a crack.

His harsh face was set in a deep frown, making him look more forbidding than usual. But when he saw her, his eyes widened in surprise. 'What beautiful hair you have!' he exclaimed.

Annabelle had removed her bonnet, freed her chestnut hair from its restraints, and, in the privacy of the cabin she shared with Rachel, let it hang in long shimmering waves down her back.

Jason looked at her with the oddest light in his eyes, and he demanded explosively, 'Why the deuce do you conceal something so lovely under that hideous bonnet?'

'Did you come merely to compliment me on my hat?' she asked in amusement.

He groaned. 'Oh, God, I've done it again. My damnable tongue. No, I came to enquire how you are faring.'

'Rachel is——'

'No need to tell me how she is. I have ears. It is you I am asking about. You need not remain with her if you are feeling ill yourself.'

This pronouncement was greeted by a wail of anguish from the berth. 'Anna, you promised!'

'I feel fine and I prefer to remain with Rachel, truly I do,' Annabelle said loudly, adding in a whisper, 'The poor child is so frightened. I have been assuring her that we will not sink.'

'I hope you may be right,' his lordship retorted wryly. 'I should not have sailed had I any notion of how severe this storm would be. Are you terrified?'

'Oh, no,' Annabelle said cheerfully. 'It is not so bad....' She had very nearly unthinkingly said, *as my return voyage from Barbados*. But she hastily bit off her words before she betrayed herself.

'"Not so bad," what?' he prompted her.

'That it makes me feel ill,' she said lamely.

'You never cease to amaze me,' Jason said with admiration. 'You are such a thin, delicate-looking thing I had expected you to be burnt to the socket and cowering in terror.'

The gleam of respect in his hard grey eyes was unmistakable, and Annabelle felt a strange pleasure. 'I am not easily frightened,' she said softly.

'Neither by the sea nor by a highwayman who holds you up on the road,' he said with a smile that Annabelle found irresistibly attractive. 'Why the deuce did you not tell me the full story of your meeting with young Walford?'

She smiled. 'You were in too much of a hurry to catch the tide and too eager to blame me for delaying you.'

Their conversation was cut short by a piteous plea from Rachel for Anna to return to her side.

An hour later the storm had broken, and Annabelle, after again swearing to Rachel that she would not leave her until they reached port, had been able to coax her to take some laudanum. The girl, exhausted from the violence of her sickness, quickly fell asleep and now, hours later, was still dead to the world.

Annabelle dressed, curbing her eagerness to go on deck to watch as the boat approached France. She would content herself with the restricted view from the porthole until Rachel awoke.

A loud hammering sounded on the door. Rachel stirred, and, without opening her eyes, called with sleepy petulance, 'Go away and leave me alone.'

In a voice that permitted no dissent, Jason called, 'We will soon dock in Dieppe. I want you on deck in half an hour.'

'I cannot possibly...' Rachel protested, her eyes still tightly closed.

He interrupted firmly, 'Half an hour, or I shall leave you aboard to sail back to England.'

That threat was enough to propel the girl from her berth like a ball from a cannon. 'You are an unfeeling monster, Jason,' she yelled angrily.

'But you've always known that,' he called back, his tone amused rather than affronted. 'If you are not on deck in half an hour, I shall go ashore and leave you aboard.'

Annabelle refrained from pointing out aloud that if he left his yacht in half an hour, given its present distance from shore, he would have a long row ahead of him to reach Dieppe. Instead, she set about helping the frantic Rachel who, her brother's threat aside, was loath to remain aboard the yacht for one more minute than was absolutely necessary.

Thirty-two minutes later, the girl emerged on deck, followed by Annabelle. Although Rachel was no longer seasick, she was still pale and wan from her earlier sufferings.

The Sea Princess was only now nearing the port, and Rachel, clearly disappointed, complained, 'But we are not yet there.'

'No, it will be a few minutes yet,' Ellerton said, consulting his watch. 'Thirty-two minutes, Rachel. I congratulate you. I did not expect you on deck in less than an hour.'

Which would be about the time they docked, Annabelle thought, wryly appreciative of the Marquess's tactic in making certain that his sister would be ready when he wished to disembark.

Annabelle moved to the polished teak railing. Ahead of them, she could see a packet in the harbour, manoeuvring to dock.

Rachel looked across the water at the farmhouses, so like the ones that they had sailed away from the previous day, dotting the round green hills of France.

'But this is England!' she exclaimed in a tone of incredulity mixed with unmistakable relief. 'The storm must have blown us back home!'

'Don't be a widgeon!' her brother said impatiently. 'That is France you see before you.'

'But it looks so like England,' Rachel said.

Annabelle was happy for this similarity. Barbados had been so different from her homeland. So flat, so hot, so humid, and, above all, so confining. At first she had revelled in the strangeness of it all, the crash of the surf beyond her windows, the exotic vegetation, the heat and intensity of the sun. But she had quickly learned how enervating the climate was.

She said to Rachel, 'Is it so strange that this part of France looks like England, when it is not all that many miles away? It is not as though we have sailed a vast distance across the open sea.'

'You mean this truly is France?' the girl asked, obviously dismayed.

Jason said in amusement, 'Why the face? It was you who insisted upon coming to France over my strenuous objections.'

'But I wanted only to visit it,' the girl wailed, 'not live here forever.'

'Nor shall you,' her brother reassured her. 'Troublesome baggage though you are, I promise to take you back to England with me.'

His words were clearly no comfort to Lady Rachel. Instead, she looked up at the rigging of *The Sea Princess* with violent loathing.

'I shall stay in France forever rather than cross the Channel again!' she exclaimed passionately. Lowering her gaze to her half-brother, she favoured him with an equally jaundiced eye. 'And *you* need not remind me of all your warnings that I should get seasick!'

The Marquess, tactful for once, refrained from reminding her of anything at all, and the conversation lapsed.

The quay at Dieppe was thronged with people, both men and women, as Ellerton's yacht docked near a large crucifix that had been erected on the pier. Did no one work in Dieppe? Annabelle wondered, before she remembered that it was Sunday.

She turned her attention to the massive fortress, faced with alternate blocks of sandstone and flint, that she had earlier glimpsed from the porthole. It was built on a hill that flanked the west side of town. A curtain wall extended from it down into Dieppe, terminating in two thick round towers with a gate between them, providing an entrance into the town from the harbour.

The packet that had docked ahead of *The Sea Princess* was still disgorging passengers when Annabelle stepped on to the pier. It was crowded with people, all of them speaking French at a furious rate. What a pleasure it was to hear the language spoken as her grand'mère, Tante Marie, and Jean-Louis had.

A wave of nostalgia washed over Annabelle as she remembered the happiness she had enjoyed with them and her father at Hillbrook. But those days were gone forever, and now she must think of the future. Her mouth tightened in determination. She must find Jean-Louis. But what if he were dead? Annabelle resolutely put this possibility from her mind. He had to be alive! And she would find him somehow!

At Annabelle's elbow, Rachel demanded crossly, 'What are all these people babbling about?'

Her brother gave her a withering look. 'You swore to me that you spoke French fluently.'

Rachel's little chin rose stubbornly. 'I do, Jason,' she insisted, 'but I speak it *correctly*.'

Lord Ellerton's dark eyebrows shot up quizzingly. 'Pray enlighten me as to what correctly means?'

'It means speaking carefully, taking care to enunciate clearly. These people are talking so rapidly and slurring their words together so badly that I can scarcely make out every tenth syllable they are saying.'

Her brother and Annabelle exchanged a speaking look, full of silent laughter, over the petite Rachel's head.

Ellerton said gravely, 'How vexingly stupid of the French not to speak their language correctly as you do. However, I strongly suggest that while in France you speak as the French speak. Unless you do not wish to be understood, in which case your *correct* French will serve you well.'

Jason offered his right arm to his sister to escort her through the throng on the quay. To Annabelle's surprise, he then gave her his left. Such politeness to a governess was unheard of, especially in a man reputed to be as rude as Lord Ellerton.

They made their way slowly through vivacious ladies, attentive gentlemen, surly soldiers, and solicitous porters. Colourful fishwomen in their grey, woven jackets, tight around their waists, and red petticoats caught Annabelle's eye. The women wore peculiar raised caps, immaculately white, with loose flaps hanging over their shoulders. Their ears were decorated with large rings or huge gold drops. They walked with a careless air, both hands thrust into their pockets, eyeing without envy some of the more fashionably dressed ladies in their high bonnets and light, flowing shawls.

Jason bundled his sister and Annabelle into a hired landau, its head folded down so that they might see the town better as they rode to what the Marquess had been assured was the very best inn in Dieppe. The faithful Putney had been left behind at *The Sea Princess* to oversee the removal of the baggage to the inn. The driver of their vehicle was a dour Frenchman in a cocked hat.

The streets were winding and narrow, shaded from the sun by lofty houses with upper stories that sported protruding balconies, elegant cornices, and curious signs.

Old women and children with strings of rosary beads and prayer books in their hands were hurrying into an ancient stone church. The minute hand of the clock in its tower pointed to the hour. Yet no church bells rang out to proclaim the time and beckon the faithful. Wondering at their absence, Annabelle stared up at the tower curiously.

Jason, who was sitting opposite her in the open landau, said, 'So you, too, noticed the absence of the bells. Very likely there are none. Most of them were melted down during the Revolution.'

Rachel, who was staring curiously at the rosaries in the churchgoers' hands, said suddenly, 'Are they craw thumpers?'

'Where did you learn that term?' her brother thundered.

His sister quailed before his anger, unconsciously revealing once again to Annabelle how afraid she was of him.

'At my aunt's,' Rachel stammered.

'I might have known!' his lordship snapped. 'Never let me hear you utter it again, nor any other expression that is derogatory to members of a faith different from your own!'

The chastised Rachel slouched unhappily down in the seat. Annabelle said nothing, but she was pleased by the Marquess's tolerance and respect for other faiths.

As the landau moved smartly up a narrow street, Annabelle asked their driver in his native tongue about the flint and sandstone castle overlooking the harbour and he told her that it had been built in the fifteenth century.

Annabelle enquired where the great palace of Jean Ango, the famous sixteenth-century privateer and governor of Dieppe, was located.

Alas, the driver told her, *le grand château* had been destroyed in 1694 by a British naval bombardment. However, Monsieur Ango's country manor still stood not far from Dieppe, near Varengeville.

'Mademoiselle is French, yes?' the driver asked her.

When she told him that she was English, he protested that she could not be. Never had he heard an *anglaise* speak French with such perfection.

'Nor have I,' Lord Ellerton said admiringly. 'How does it happen that you speak the language as though you were born and raised here. Did you once live here?'

'No, but my grandmother, who helped raise me, was French, and she liked to talk to me in her native tongue.' Annabelle did not mention either Tante Marie or Jean-Louis. That could lead to more questions by the Marquess that she did not want to answer.

'Was it your grand'mère who told you about Jean Ango?' Jason asked.

'Who was he?' Rachel interjected.

Annabelle, seizing the opportunity to direct the conversation away from herself and impart a little history to her pupil in the process, explained that Jean Ango was a sixteenth-century shipbuilder and maritime counsellor to King François. When the Portuguese began treating ships of other nations sailing off the coast of Africa as pirates, the French

decided to retaliate. Ango constructed and led a
fleet of privateers which, within a few years, captured more than three hundred Portuguese ships.
That nation's king had been forced to pay a
handsome price to the French ruler to withdraw the
letters of marque under which Ango and his privateer navy operated. Later the king had appointed
Ango governor of Dieppe.

The carriage stopped in front of 'the very best
inn' in Dieppe. Although impressive in size and architecture, the building showed signs of neglect. The
flowers in the window boxes were dying from lack
of attention, while exceedingly healthy strands of
tall grass were growing vigorously between the grey
slates of the roof. Nevertheless, it was superior to
the other hostelries that they had passed, some of
which had cracked windows and gaping holes in
their roofs.

As Annabelle listened to Jason make known to
the innkeeper his wishes regarding rooms, dinner,
and the private parlour in which he wished it served,
she discovered that his fluency in French matched
her own.

When she told him so, he replied carelessly, 'I
have my French mother to thank; she instructed me
diligently in her native tongue.'

Rachel and Annabelle were shown to a spacious
room that would have been rather elegant had it
not been in disrepair and less than spotlessly clean.
It had a magnificent marble chimneypiece and
several impressively large mirrors in elaborately
carved and gilded frames. At least once they had

been gilt. Now most of it had worn off. The silk covering the walls was so faded that it was impossible to tell its original shade. But there was a marble-topped commode and a gold washbasin. Annabelle suspected that both items had been looted from a rich noble's estate during the Revolution.

She was happy that the room was large and comfortable, for she had often had to settle for much more primitive lodgings during her travels with her father in the Americas. But Lady Rachel, gold washbasin notwithstanding, turned up her pert little nose and attempted to convey her displeasure to the innkeeper, who instantly developed a profound ignorance of English.

She asked Annabelle to translate her complaints into French, but her brother, overhearing her, came into the room. 'You must make your own complaints,' he told his sister. 'I forbid Miss Smith to make them for you. Since I am her employer, not you, she cannot disobey me. So do not plague her to do so.' He looked about the chamber that had been assigned to his sister and her governess. 'I find this room quite acceptable for you.'

When Rachel began to pout, he said in a quelling tone, 'I warned you accommodations in France would not always be of the quality to which you have been accustomed, and you assured me that you did not care. If you now discover that you do care, you have only to tell me so, and I shall be happy to dispatch you back to England aboard *The Sea Princess*.'

The threat instantly ended Rachel's complaints. She passionately declared that she preferred death to recrossing the Channel.

Annabelle suspected his lordship was very astute when it came to divining the best way to get females to do his bidding.

Later, as they were dressing for dinner, Rachel had difficulty deciding which gown she wished to wear for her first dinner in France. She vacillated between her spotted muslin, lilac sarcenet, and white cambric. By the time Annabelle had helped the girl into her belated choice, a dainty sprig muslin, and had arranged her hair, it was time to join Lord Ellerton in the private parlour for dinner.

Knowing how much the Marquess resented being kept waiting, she sent Rachel downstairs with word to begin the meal without her while she hastily coiled her long chestnut tresses atop her head.

When Annabelle joined the Marquess and his sister, however, she found that they had waited for her in a tense, uneasy silence. He was standing near a long window, his back to the room, looking out at a small garden behind the inn while Rachel sat on the edge of a chair in the corner casting nervous glances in his direction.

Hearing Annabelle enter the room, his lordship turned towards her with such a look of relief on his face that she was startled. Why, the Notorious Marquess is as uncomfortable with his little sister as she is with him, Annabelle thought in amusement.

As she advanced into the room, Lord Ellerton looked her over with such a critical eye that she was humiliatingly conscious of how dowdy and un-fashionable her black Cyprus crêpe dinner gown, another one of Tante Marie's mourning dresses that she had altered for herself, must look to him. She was several inches taller than her aunt, and she had been forced to remedy the difference in height by inserting a band of material at the waist and adding a ruffle to the skirt. Unfortunately, she had no more of the dress's material and instead had had to use lustring purloined from one of Tante Marie's pet-ticoats. It was clear from the way the Marquess's gaze checked briefly at the waist and ruffle that the makeshift addition had not escaped his sharp eye.

She wondered if he would make some uncivil remark about her gown as he had about her bonnet on board *The Sea Princess*, and she schooled her face to remain impassive.

But when he spoke to her, it was to say with un-impeachable politeness that he hoped the dinner would meet her approval, but that he rather doubted it would since the chef's culinary reper-toire seemed to be confined to soups and stews.

'You should have begun dinner without me, as I requested,' Annabelle told him.

'But that would have been unpardonably rude, even for one as notorious for his incivility as I am,' he said, a gleam of self-mockery softening his silver-grey eyes.

The dinner began with a turbot soup followed by a beef stew. Both were very good. Now that Annabelle had escaped England and her brother, her appetite revived, and she consumed in addition to the soup two large bowls of stew and a generous portion of the excellent crême de fraises that was the meal's finale.

'I believe you enjoyed the dinner,' Ellerton said drily as she ate the last morsel of her dessert. 'To look at you, one would think you had the appetite of a baby wren.'

She hid her embarrassment at his having observed her eating like a yeoman behind a smile. 'Appearances can be deceiving,' she retorted lightly.

But he did not return her smile. Instead, his eyes studied her searchingly. 'Especially, I think, in your case.'

Annabelle wondered uneasily whether he could have begun to suspect the truth about her. Her own thoughts were in considerable confusion. His conversation during dinner had been an entertaining mixture of anecdotes and astute observations on a variety of subjects. His ironic cast of mind and turn of phrase delighted her.

By the end of the meal Annabelle realised how wrong she had been when she had told him he was not in the least charming. Not since that long-ago time at Hillbrook when her father had entertained his friends, picked for their conversational ability, had she so enjoyed a dinner.

But Annabelle's pleasure was not shared by Lady Rachel, who did not understand her brother's sardonic humour and took it seriously.

When a servant entered with a bottle of brandy for Jason, his sister, eager to escape his company as quickly as possible, said, 'I am so tired, Jason. May I be excused?'

He nodded, and she bolted for the door like a prisoner freed from Newgate.

As Annabelle rose to follow the girl from the room, leaving Ellerton with his brandy, she renewed her vow to bring brother and sister to a better understanding of each other.

CHAPTER TEN

As Annabelle helped Rachel undress, the girl asked whether her brother knew yet about Eustace's attempt to abduct her. When she was told that he did, she said dubiously. 'Are you certain? He has said nothing to me, and I expected him to ring such a dreadful peal over me.'

'He understands that it was not your fault. Your brother is not the ogre that you think him.'

'You don't know him!'

'I think it is you who do not know him,' Annabelle said gently.

But Rachel was clearly unconvinced. A minute later she asked, 'Anna, what is the Whittington's college that you mentioned to Eustace?'

'Newgate Prison.'

'Why is it called that?'

'I think because Dick Whittington left money to repair it,' Annabelle replied. 'Did you know that his cat is carved in bas-relief upon its gates? And college is a cant term for a prison.'

After Rachel was in bed, Annabelle discovered that she was far too wide awake to contemplate sleep. The night was hot and so was their room. The garden that Annabelle had glimpsed behind the inn would be more pleasant, and she went down to it.

As she stepped outside, a big, bright moon bathed the garden in its pale light. The back half of the plot was devoted to the utilitarian purpose of providing fresh herbs and vegetables for the inn's guests, but the front portion had been planted with grass and flowers, including several rosebushes, and a long bench had been placed there for visitors to sit upon.

Settling on the bench, Annabelle looked up at the moon, which was retreating from fullness, its perfect roundness spoiled by a flattened edge.

'May I join you, Anna?' Lord Ellerton called from the doorway that she had come through a few minutes earlier.

She was startled into retorting, 'I would think that you would prefer your brandy to the company of a governess.'

'Oh, I am quite democratic,' he told her mockingly. 'And I have never cared for solitary drinking.'

He strode to the bench where Annabelle was sitting. The delicate moonlight softened his sharp features.

Annabelle would have risen, but he bade her remain seated. Since it was the only bench in the garden, politeness dictated that she ask him to sit there, too. He did so, settling nearer to her than she would have liked. Something about his closeness was strangely unnerving to her.

Without preamble, he asked in that abrupt manner of his, 'What do you think of my sister?'

'I own I am pleasantly surprised.'

'Don't try to gammon me,' he said sharply. 'She is a sullen brat.'

'I thought that at first, too, but it is not her natural disposition.' Annabelle quickly sketched for him the details of the circumscribed, boring life that Rachel had led as she grew up, sequestered at Elmdale's dower house with her mother.

'Indeed, my heart goes out to her,' Annabelle said. 'She is a bright, lively girl who has had both mind and spirit squelched. Her mother hired her governesses for their sternness rather than for any intelligence or skill with children. As a result, the poor girl is convinced that all governesses are enemies to be outwitted.'

'She no longer seems to regard you that way,' Jason observed.

'No, because I have demonstrated to her that I am not her enemy. But I collect now why Claire had such difficulty. Not only was she a hated governess, but she was hired by you, which put her beyond the pale in Rachel's view.'

His face, in the light of the moon, was startled. 'Are you telling me that I am sunk beneath reproach in my sister's eyes?'

Annabelle nodded. 'Rachel is terrified of you.'

'Terrified?' he challenged. 'Come now, doing it rather too brown, aren't you?'

'No, it is true. Not to wrap it in clean linen, she has been convinced for years that you are a vile ogre.'

Temptation novels bring you all the joy and tenderness of age-old romance, experienced in contemporary love affairs...

And to introduce you to this powerful, highly charged series, we'll send you *4 Temptation books* absolutely **FREE** when you complete and return this card.

We're so confident that you'll enjoy Temptations that we'll also reserve a subscription for you, to the Mills & Boon Reader Service, which means you could enjoy...

- *FOUR BRAND NEW NOVELS* – sent direct to you every month (before they're available in the shops)
- *FREE POSTAGE & PACKING* – we pay all the extras.
- *FREE REGULAR NEWSLETTER* – packed with special offers, competitions, author news and much, much more...

FOUR

IRRESISTIBLY
CAPTIVATING
NOVELS

FREE!
★☆ PLUS ☆★

YOURS FREE!

This cuddly Teddy Bear measures 5 inches sitting down. His brown eyes and cute expression make him the perfect lucky mascot!

★☆ **PLUS** ☆★

A SURPRISE
MYSTERY
GIFT

>>>> CLAIM THESE GIFTS OVERLEAF >>>>

FREE BOOKS CERTIFICATE

Yes! Please send me my **4 Free Temptations** together with my **FREE GIFTS**. Please also reserve a special Reader Service Subscription for me. If I decide to subscribe, I shall receive 4 superb Temptations every month for just £5.40 post and packing free. If I decide not to subscribe I shall write to you within 10 days. The free books and gifts will be mine to keep in any case. **I understand that I am under no obligation whatsoever** - I can cancel or suspend my subscription at any time simply by writing to you. *I am over 18 years of age*

2AOT

NAME _____

ADDRESS _____

_____

_____ POSTCODE _____

SIGNATURE _____

FREE GIFT

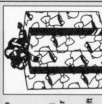

Return this card now and we'll also send you this cuddly Teddy Bear absolutely FREE together with...

A SURPRISE MYSTERY GIFT.

We all love surprises, so as well as the FREE books and Teddy Bear there's an intriguing mystery gift especially for you.

POST TODAY!

NO
STAMP
NEEDED

MILLS & BOON
FREEPOST
P.O. BOX 236
CROYDON
CR9 9EL

'Good God, why? Until a month ago she had not laid eyes on me above half a dozen times in her life.'

'That *is* why.' Annabelle told him how his stepmother had used him to try to frighten her daughter into obedience. 'Since Rachel never saw you, she had nothing to contradict the dreadful picture of you that her mother painted.'

'But surely a month under my roof has demonstrated to her that I am no ogre.'

'It has enhanced rather than dispelled that opinion.'

'Don't hoax me! What possible unkindness can she accuse me of?'

'Of dragging her away from her aunt's, the only place where the poor child ever had any fun. It cannot be very exciting beneath your roof, since you ignore her.'

'I have given her everything she has asked for,' he said indignantly.

'Rachel is not one of your convenients to be indulged and then ignored as the spirit moves you.'

'You are impertinent!'

'Yes, I am,' she acknowledged cheerfully, 'but it appears that I must be if I am to make you understand what the girl needs. You may have granted her material requests, but you have not given her either your attention or affection, and she desperately needs both. Indeed, my lord, it is my impression that you are very nearly as uncomfortable in Rachel's presence as she is in yours.'

'You are right!' he admitted ruefully. 'What do I know about schoolroom misses? And what the deuce am I to talk to her about when she is so gloweringly silent and seems utterly incapable of any conversation. I had concluded that the chit was as shatterbrained as her mother before her.'

'Oh, no, she is not. I doubt that anyone could be—— Oh dear, I did not mean to insult the late Marchioness. I beg your pardon,' Annabelle exclaimed in embarrassment.

'Don't apologise on my account,' he said drily. 'I am in complete agreement with your assessment of my stepmother. How my father came to rue the day he had let himself be talked into marrying her!'

Annabelle raised her brows enquiringly. 'By whom?'

'Her father, Sir Thomas Steele.'

Annabelle remembered that her own papa had disliked Sir Thomas excessively, branding him as one of the most ambitious and underhanded men that he had ever known.

Ellerton said, 'There was a period in my life when I was young that I seemed hell-bent on getting myself killed. I duelled with anyone who wished to oblige me, and a fair number did. Sir Thomas convinced my father that I would most likely die before him, leaving him without an heir, and that he must remarry to father another son. No one, Sir Thomas insisted, would be a better choice for this second wife than his own daughter.' Jason's voice dripped with sarcasm and a sneer twisted his hard face. 'The fact that she was not yet out of the schoolroom was a great advantage, assuring she would be both malleable and fertile. My father was in ill health even then. Sir Thomas thought that he would soon die, leaving behind an infant son in the guardianship of his maternal grandfather. Sir Thomas would then control the vast Ellerton inheritance. But his scheme failed when his daughter did not produce a son.'

'It would not have signified if she had,' Annabelle said. 'You were still the heir.'

'Sir Thomas did his best to cure that. I was several times challenged to duels by men I have strong reason to believe were well paid by Sir Thomas to do so. Unfortunately for him, I was the victor.'

'How dreadful!' Annabelle exclaimed. 'Surely he——'

'Never underestimate what a man will do when great money or power is at stake,' Jason said bitterly.

Annabelle shuddered. 'No wonder you did not like his daughter.'

'But not for that reason. The peagoose was as much her papa's victim as my own father was. Think how dreadful it must have been to a shy, timid girl of sixteen, whose empty head held nothing but romantic dreams, to be forced to marry an ailing martinet, three times her age, whom she both feared and disliked. He, in turn, expected her to run his household and entertain his guests with all the skill that my mother had, when the poor little mouse had no experience nor inclination for either.'

Annabelle was startled by how much sympathy and understanding the Marquess exhibited for his stepmother's situation, even though he clearly did not like her.

'What disgusted me about her,' he continued, 'was her unrelieved sloth and bottomless supply of self-pity. Instead of coming to terms with her life and trying to make the best of it, she did nothing but lie upon her couch day after day, feeling sorry for herself, eating confections, and growing enormously fat. She ignored her husband, her household, and even her child. She escaped the demands upon her, and indeed life itself, by retiring to a sickbed with feigned illnesses. She so aggravated my father that his friends blamed her for causing his fatal seizure.'

Jason jumped up from the bench and began pacing in a small circle in front of it. 'After my father's death I had to oversee the running of the dower house as well as the big house at Elmdale because she could not bestir herself. Several times in the beginning I was so exasperated with her that I gave her stiff lectures on her responsibilities, especially towards her daughter. I collect that is where she got the notion that I might try to take Rachel away from her. After that, whenever I tried to talk to her, she would take to her bed, insisting that she was far too ill to see me.'

His father's second marriage had been as disastrous as Annabelle's own papa's. Frederick's mother had been every bit as ambitious and cunning as Rachel's grandfather, and she had set her trap for the Earl of Chilton while he was still grieving for Annabelle's mother. When the late Earl had discovered his bride's true nature, even the well-publicised loathing the Prince Regent had for his consort, Princess Charlotte, paled beside that Annabelle's father had felt for his second wife. Indeed, Annabelle had often suspected that he had remained so many years in the West Indies because he could not bear to be in the same country with his estranged wife. It had only been after he learned of her death that he had decided to live again in England.

Annabelle said quietly, 'Your sister does not take after her mother.'

Jason stopped his pacing and again took a seat beside Annabelle on the bench. 'That is not the impression that Rachel has given me.'

'I am not surprised. Even had her mother not deliberately cultivated her fear of you, your manner is so blunt and abrupt that it cannot fail to intimidate a girl as sheltered from social intercourse as Rachel has been. Furthermore, she is too young and naïve to comprehend your ironic humour. She thinks you are serious. And, of course, she cannot forgive you for removing her from her aunt's.'

'I would have been delighted to leave Rachel there, but the woman was almost as great a goose-cap as my stepmother. Her doors were open to men'—he checked himself abruptly, finishing rather lamely—'who, for various reasons, Rachel should not be permitted to know. It would be disastrous should one of them fix her interest.'

'I collect,' Annabelle said, an amused gleam in her eye, 'that in addition to gazetted fortune hunters like young Walford, Rachel ran the danger of meeting men with your sort of reputation.'

'Precisely! You cannot imagine that I would permit her to marry a man like myself!'

'How *very* wise of you,' Annabelle agreed approvingly.

'Yes, isn't it?' he returned affably, refusing to be baited. 'I may be a libertine, but I am not a fool.'

'Clearly, you have your sister's best interests at heart,' Annabelle conceded with a smile, 'but you can see why she cannot comprehend that.'

There was no mistaking, even in the weak light of the moon, the admiration in his eyes. 'Now I can, and I appreciate your round dealing with me. A woman who tells me what I need to hear instead of what she thinks I want to hear is a very rare experience for me. I am in Mrs Potter's debt for having brought you to me. She said that you met while she was the governess for Chilton's daughter. Did you know the Earl well?'

'Very well,' Annabelle admitted.

'I liked and respected him,' Jason said thoughtfully. 'The *ton* thought him eccentric because he preferred his scientific interests and intellectual companions to their company, but I liked him the better for it.'

And Annabelle liked the Marquess better for his high opinion of her beloved father.

'We used to have some lively conversations, he and I, and I missed him after he went to the West

Indies to take charge personally of his failing plantation there. I was told it took him several years, but he succeeded in making it very profitable again.'

Jason had been told correctly. Her father's lucrative plantation on Barbados had been heavily planted in cotton, but over the years competition by the former English colonies in the southern United States had increased until seven years ago the market for Barbados cotton had vanished. Her father, an amateur botanist, had gone to the island to oversee replanting his land with Bourbon cane, a new strain of sugar cane that had a much higher yield than earlier varieties. Now the income from his plantation—actually *her* plantation, since it was one of the properties her father had left her—was richer than ever.

Jason said, 'He quite shocked the *ton*, though, by taking his daughter to live there with him. She was very popular in London society, and they thought it exceedingly cruel of him to drag her away from it. Lady Barbara, I think her name was, or was it Belle?'

Annabelle, uneasy with the turn the conversation had taken, said hastily, 'Belle.'

'Whatever,' Jason said with a negligent shrug. 'She attracted an impressive number of highly eligible suitors after her come-out in addition to the usual contingent of fortune hunters who always pursue an heiress of her considerable expectations. I saw her once, and I own I was surprised that she had created such a stir, for she was no beauty.

Indeed, she was so unmemorable that I would not have recognised her again if I saw her.'

Annabelle should have been exceedingly grateful for that, but it gave her no pleasure at all to discover how forgettable Jason had found her.

'Clearly Lady Belle set too high a store by herself,' he said critically. 'She rejected several very advantageous offers and probably ended up an ape leader for her choosiness.'

Stung by his interpretation of her spinsterhood, Annabelle asked sharply, 'Is that why you have never married. You have been unable to secure a sufficiently advantageous match?'

He looked startled. 'I have no need to marry for advantage and no desire to marry at all.'

'Perhaps Lady Belle felt the same way!'

'Ladies of quality never feel that way!' he said scornfully. 'They are always determined to catch some poor fool in parson's mousetrap. It doesn't much matter who so long as he has blunt and breeding.'

He spoke with such bitterness that Annabelle wondered what woman had inspired it. To her knowledge, the only lady of quality he had ever been linked with had been Lord Ivly's daughter, and he had treated her abominably.

'Did you meet Chilton's son?' he asked abruptly. 'I know that he did not live with his father. It was just as well the old Earl spent his last years abroad, where he did not know what a little snake his heir is. The father was an honest and honourable man, and his son could only have caused him immeasurable grief.'

Annabelle was startled at how close Jason's opinion in this regard coincided with her own. 'It is my impression that the new Earl, despite his title, is not liked by his peers,' she observed, thinking that perhaps Ellerton could shed some light on why this was the case.

'No, he is not, even though he toad-eats them odiously.'

'Does he toad-eat you?' she asked, remembering how violent Frederick's hatred of Ellerton had been.

'Not any more. He would put a blade through my back if he could.'

'Your back!'

Jason grinned sardonically. 'He is far too cowardly a little sneak to confront me to my face.'

'What earned you his enmity?'

'My sharp eyes. Three years ago I caught him trying to prig the Duchess of Stratford's diamond bracelet.'

'You're joking!' Annabelle gasped, unable to believe her half brother could have sunk that low. 'Surely he would not steal.'

'Let me say that he made the most of an opportunity when it presented itself. It happened at one of Lady Pomroy's squeezes. The bracelet must not have been properly fastened, and it fell from the Duchess's wrist as she arose from a divan. She did not notice that she had lost it, but Chilton's sprig did. He hastily sat down on the divan and surreptitiously pocketed the bracelet. I was standing some distance away, and he did not notice that I was watching him.'

Annabelle had been aware that her brother suffered from serious defects in his character, but she would never have thought him capable of such shocking behaviour. 'What did you do?'

'When he tried to slip out of the room, I cornered him and ordered him to return the bracelet to the Duchess.' The harsh lines of Jason's face tightened perceptibly in the moonlight. 'He professed not to know what I was talking about. I threatened to turn him upside down in front of everyone and shake the bracelet from his pocket. The Duchess soon had it back.'

'So that is why he hates you.'

'Only partly why. A few months ago I caught him palming a card while he was playing at White's and called him on it. I had said nothing to anyone about the bracelet, but there was a large and fascinated audience for our confrontation at White's.' A dark cloud drifted across the lopsided moon, casting Jason's face into shadow. 'Until then, young Chilton had enjoyed extraordinary luck at play. A great many people suspected that it was not luck at all. After I verified the truth of their suspicions by exposing him, he was blackballed by the better clubs. He had never been popular among the *ton*, and his exposure as a card cheat made him considerably less so.'

To cover her agitation at these revelations about her half-brother, Annabelle got up from the bench and walked over to one of the rosebushes, pretending to examine its flowers. 'He is a rich man,' she pointed out. 'Why would he find it necessary to cheat at cards?'

'Greed. He is one of those close-fisted men who, no matter how much money they have, can never have enough and hate to part with so much as a shilling of what they do have. Only that kind of mindless, overriding greed could have prompted him to marry that old cloth-merchant's tedious, *déclassé* granddaughter.'

'What?' Annabelle gasped.

'It is well known that the old merchant paid an exorbitant sum to make his granddaughter a countess.'

So that was why Frederick had married Hetty. Revolted as Annabelle was by Jason's reading of her brother's character, she feared that it was correct. To hide the tears forming in her eyes, she lowered her head to the rosebush on the pretence of sniffing one of its big yellow blooms. It was a minute before she could regain sufficient command of her voice to observe, 'Not a very handsome picture you paint of young Lord Chilton.'

'I doubt that there is anything handsome about that dandy! His tailors have their work cut out for them.'

They lapsed into silence. Annabelle wondered uneasily what her unprincipled brother would do when he returned to London on the morrow from Budwell Abbey and discovered that she had vanished.

CHAPTER ELEVEN

FREDERICK was already in sour humour when he arrived at his house in Berkeley Street that Monday, even though he was not yet aware that Annabelle had fled from it. He had long coveted an invitation to one of Lord and Lady Chapman's famous weekend parties at Budwell Abbey, their country seat not far from London. So eager had he been for this invitation he had gone so far as to make Lord Chapman, who had been in dun territory of late, a small loan. For Frederick this was very far indeed. But Lord Chapman belonged to a rarefied element of society that young Chilton was desperate to have accept him. Frederick would not have permitted anything to stop him from going to Budwell Abbey, even his sister's inconvenient arrival in London.

His four days at Budwell Abbey had not gone as he had expected they would. It had been only a very small party that had not included any of Lord Chapman's more illustrious friends. The host's only interest in Frederick had been in securing another loan, this time of a large sum of money for an indefinite period at no interest.

Now that Frederick was back in London, he would have to face his maddening sister. If the truth be known, he was a little afraid of her. She was so calm and capable and quick-witted. Frederick, who had a nervous, irritable disposition, was baffled by a woman who seemed to have no nerves and who refused to accord him the deference and obedience that was his due.

How he hated her. He was the son and rightful heir, but their father had left her all of his great fortune that had not been entailed. A less greedy man would have been grateful that the entail was as large as it was, but Frederick had been outraged because it was so much smaller than Annabelle's inheritance. He unconsciously clenched his hands into fists at the unjustness of his father's action. But in the end, Frederick thought proudly, he had outwitted his father.

The late Earl's will had stated only that his daughter's inheritance was to be held in trust and had named the trustees. But a second document that Frederick had taken care that Annabelle should not see had contained very specific instructions for the trust. Under it, all of her expenses were to be paid by her trustee. Since she was, in theory at least, a member of Frederick's household, he had liberally interpreted this provision to mean that the trust should pay all the expenses for Hillbrook and his London house as well as Moorlands. It had also stipulated that she was to receive two thousand pounds a year in pin money. Frederick had dutifully withdrawn these funds on the pretext of paying them to Annabelle and had pocketed them himself.

He had been aided and abetted in his misappropriation of his sister's money by his solicitor, Ruben

Quigg. Frederick had lied to Annabelle when he had said that their father had named Mr Quigg to succeed his incapacitated uncle as the Earl's man of business. In fact, their father had refused to have anything to do with Quigg, even though he was old Mr Barbour's nephew, dismissing him as a shifty-eyed, untrustworthy cove. But, fortunately for Frederick's schemes, his father had not yet had time to select a new solicitor before his unexpected death.

Frederick had been quite willing to give the eager Mr Quigg the position if he, in turn, aided the new Lord Chilton in obtaining the benefit of his sister's inheritance, which should have been rightfully his anyhow. At first Quigg had been reluctant. It had taken a generous additional sum from Frederick to overcome the solicitor's hesitation.

By the time Annabelle, still ignorant of her father's death, had returned to England, Frederick had had plenty of time to put his scheme into operation. He had not seen his half-sister since he was nine years old, and he had expected her to be a typical long-toothed spinster, timid and easily cowed. He had never dreamed that she would turn out to be such a determined and independent woman. She had refused to accept Quigg's word on her trust and had sought the advice of another solicitor, who had had to be bribed with an indecently large sum of money to second Quigg's opinion.

Frederick's greatest fear was that his sister would marry. Despite what she had been told, control of her inheritance would pass from her brother to her husband if she married, and Frederick was determined to see that never happened. Although she seemed firmly on the shelf, Frederick was taking no chances. To keep her from meeting any eligible men, he had manipulated her into going to Moorlands, where she would be isolated from society.

And now he would have to get her back there again, he thought, as he stalked into his house. The last place on earth he wanted her was in London with its many bachelors and determined fortune-hunters.

He nearly collided with Hetty in the entry hall. It could not be said that he was happy to see her. He had not had an iota of interest in her since that day, two months after their wedding, when her wily old grandfather had paid the third and final instalment of the huge sum that Frederick had demanded as a condition of making Hetty his Countess.

'Send Annabelle to me,' he told his spouse by way of greeting.

Hetty, looking frightened, stammered, 'She...she has disappeared.'

'Disappeared,' Frederick cried, aghast.

The news was sufficiently alarming to send him scurrying to Mr Quigg's shabby office in a back street of the city. There, his accomplice offered him no comfort.

'If she goes to see my uncle, we are dished,' Quigg predicted gloomily. 'The old man ain't what he once was, but he's improved enough by now that he'd see things straight if he learned the way it is with her. He knows better than anyone what the terms of the trust are, and he'll waste no time in telling her. He never did like me.' Wouldn't surprise me none,' Quigg continued pessimistically, 'if that plaguey sister of yours don't marry the first man she can. If she does, you better hope she picks a muttonhead who isn't going to be demanding an accounting of her money.'

Above all else, Frederick had to prevent Annabelle from marrying. But how was he to do that when he had no idea where she was? The only possible solution, he decided in panicked desperation, was to blacken her reputation so badly that no decent man would consider shackling himself to her.

He set out immediately to do so, beginning his campaign with his wife, telling her that he had discovered to his shock and horror his sister had run off with a lover and undoubtedly was even now lying in his arms.

Hetty, always eager to think the worst of everyone, confessed that she had always thought Annabelle a bold piece, and now that she knew the truth, she could never again welcome her beneath her roof.

'No, of course not,' her husband agreed. 'Nor will I subject you to the company of such an immoral woman. If I can find her and remove her from her scandalous position, I will insist that she live at Moorlands.'

After leaving Hetty, Frederick made it a point to inform everyone he met that Annabelle had run off with a secret lover whose identity he was doing his best to discover.

Frederick reasoned that once he found Annabelle, he would return her to the isolation of Moorlands, where she could not challenge the veracity of the slanderous story about her. Then he would tell everyone that she had gone there because she was too ashamed to face the world after her lover had refused to marry her. It was a brilliant scheme, Frederick thought proudly.

He sought out one man in particular, Lord Rudolph Oldfield, the most malicious gossip in London. Frederick knew that no one could spread the story of his sister's fictional indiscretion quicker than Oldfield. To Frederick's disappointment, he found his lordship preparing to depart for France.

'Everyone who is anyone is going there, my dear boy,' Oldfield assured him.

'When do you leave?' Frederick asked in alarm.

'In five days.'

Frederick was vastly relieved. That would give Oldfield more than enough time to make Annabelle the scandal of London.

CHAPTER TWELVE

WHEN Jason and his party set out from Dieppe
upon the road to Paris, Annabelle and Rachel were
ensconced in a *diligence de ville*, a French version
of a post-chaise. Jason, who wished to reach Paris
as quickly as possible, had ordered four horses instead of a pair for the *diligence*, even though this
meant two postilions instead of one.

He himself was mounted on a spirited grey, the
best the stables of Dieppe had had to offer. In
drawing up instructions for the journey prior to
leaving England, he had been loath to travel from
Dieppe to Paris trapped in a coach with his sullen
sister, and so he had ordered a horse for himself.

It had been his intention to travel in this manner
all the way to Paris, but by the time he mounted
the grey in front of the inn in Dieppe he was re-
gretting his decision. While he still had little taste
for his sister's company, he was developing a strong
one for Anna's. He was baffled, given his pref-
erence for beautiful high fliers, why he should find
himself so intrigued by this thin, plain spinster.

His regret that he had not opted for the *diligence*
increased as the day progressed, and he grew more
and more bored with the monotonous landscape of
the Caux plateau through which they were travelling. Whenever his sister's tinkling young laugh

rang out from inside the carriage, he found himself
wondering what Anna had said to prompt it.

It occurred to him that he had never, before
Anna's advent, heard Rachel laugh. What a difference she had made in the girl in only a couple
of days. He was somewhat chagrined that Anna
had managed to learn more about his sister in that
short time than he had in the several weeks that she
had been beneath his roof. He was generally an
astute judge of people, but he had been prejudiced
against the chit because of her annoying behaviour.
It had reminded him so much of her mother that
he had immediately assumed that she was like her.
Now, thanks to Anna, he realised that he had been
wrong, and he felt considerably more sympathetic
towards Rachel. Jason promised himself that in the
future he would be more attentive and patient with
her.

How Anna had managed to win the girl's confidence and learn so much about her in such a short
time was beyond him. Then, realising how much
he was looking forward to dinner when he could
again enjoy Anna's company, he had to grudgingly
admit that she had dissolved his own initial hostility towards her as easily as she had Rachel's.

Anna's company at dinner that night did not dis-
appoint Jason, and the following morning he
abandoned his horse in favour of the *diligence*.
Rachel was not pleased with this new arrangement
and sank into a fit of the sullens at the prospect of
having to spend the day in such close quarters with

the brother she feared. But Anna soon coaxed the girl out of her freakish temper.

Jason did not regret his decision to ride in the *diligence*. Indeed, in the days that followed, as they drove through the fields of Normandy with their tall windbreaks of oak and elm and beech protecting apple trees and half-timbered farmhouses, nothing would have induced him to retreat to a horse. He was as much entertained as Rachel as he listened to Anna telling his sister the history of the duchy of Normandy.

Rachel was spellbound by Anna's dramatic tales of the Viking Rollo, the leader of the Normans who had been granted the duchy upon its creation in 911 by the king of France, and of Rollo's descendents, Emma, mother of England's king, Edward the Confessor, and her brother, Robert. Annabelle told of Robert's love for Arlette, the daughter of a tanner, who bore him a bastard son, William, and of William's stormy courtship of the proud Matilda of Flanders. In the end, William, who had succeeded his father as duke, conquered both Matilda's pride and her heart, and she came to love him well.

'Your stories are more exciting than a novel,' Rachel said, enthralled.

Anna contended that when William later conquered England, he was justified in doing so because he had been designated the heir of his cousin, Edward the Confessor, the childless King of England. But Harold, son of a powerful Earl, had usurped the throne upon Edward's death.

Jason, whose reading of history favoured the Saxons' claim over the Norman Duke's, disputed this, insisting that William, not Harold, was the usurper. Rachel listened wide-eyed to the spirited but good-humoured argument that ensued between her brother and Anna.

'You mean that the William you are talking about, Matilda's husband, was William the Conqueror?' Rachel asked. 'But I have heard of him.'

'I cannot conceive how you should have heard of such an obscure king,' her brother said drily.

Rachel looked at him uncertainly.

'He is funning you,' Annabelle said.

But the girl was unpersuaded. 'Are you truly, Jason?

'Of course I am, puss,' he assured her. Anna had been right. The girl did not understand his humour at all. He remembered ruefully how, when she had first come to live with him, he had tried to tease her out of her perpetual fit of the sullens. He had been baffled when this had made her only retreat deeper into glowering hostility, but now he understood that she had taken his quizzing seriously.

Anna had a remarkable talent for bringing history and its characters from Julius Caesar and Eleanor of Aquitaine to Richard the Lionheart and Joan of Arc vividly alive. When she talked of the late Empress Josephine's childhood in the West Indies, she spoke with such authority that Jason would almost have thought she had seen those remote islands.

By the time they reached Rouen, Normandy's capital, Rachel had learned a great deal about French and English history and other subjects as well. Anna would casually identify various trees and plants, point out the details that differentiated Romanesque from Gothic and Renaissance architecture, or discuss the social injustices that had given rise to the French Revolution. Rachel, who was woefully ignorant in history, art, and science, would have been astonished to realise that Anna was giving her skilfully disguised lessons that she would have scorned had she recognised them for what they were.

What a very clever woman Miss Smith was, Jason thought admiringly. Yet, despite her considerable knowledge and quick mind, there was not the slightest hint of a bluestocking's serious, pedantic cast of mind. She had too lively a sense of humour.

Darkness had fallen by the time they reached the outskirts of Rouen. The road straightened into a broad, straight avenue lined on each side by the silhouettes of impressively tall trees. Large lamps hung over the centre of the road, suspended from ropes fastened to the trees on either side, illuminating their path. They drove to their inn through streets crowded with people making their way in or out of theatres and cafés. Small groups of spectators congregated around ballad-singers at several street corners.

The following morning Rachel, her interest fired by Anna's stories, prevailed upon Jason to delay their departure from Rouen for a few hours so that

she might view the Place de Vieux Marché, where
Joan of Arc had been burned at the stake, and the
great cathedral containing the tomb of Richard the
Lionheart.

'Oh,' Rachel exclaimed in disappointment when
she saw the cathedral with its dissimilar towers,
'why do they not match as other churches' do?'

'They were built in different centuries,' Anna
said. 'The St Romanus Tower on the left was constructed in the twelfth century, and the Butter Tower
on the right in the fifteenth——'

'Why is it called the Butter Tower?' Rachel
interjected.

'Because it was reportedly financed by those who
bought dispensations allowing them to eat butter
during Lent,' Anna said, adding wryly, 'However,
it was never finished, so perhaps not enough people
in the fifteenth century wished to eat butter during
Lent.'

As they examined the exterior of the cathedral,
Jason listened to his two companions discussing its
various aspects. He could listen to Anna's arresting
voice, as warm and sensuous as a caress, all day.
And all night, too. The thought shocked him, and
he wondered if he had taken leave of his senses. As
she had told him the day he had met her, she was
not at all his style. But she was proving to be more
entertaining than any of those dazzling demi-reps
he had had under his protection.

She was remarkably knowledgeable for a woman
who had spent her life in a rural backwater. In fact,
except for her dreadfully outmoded clothes, she did

not seem at all provincial. Jason wondered what she would look like in fashionable gowns instead of those cast-offs that were clearly all she possessed. Nor did black become her at all. Had she once been able to afford stylish clothes, back before her father had lost his handsome property?

He asked abruptly, 'When did your father die?'

Much startled, she answered, 'It will be a year next week.'

'So you will soon be out of mourning.'

'Yes, but I cannot see of what interest that is to you.'

He shrugged carelessly. 'None at all,' he lied. But it was. Her colouring cried out for vivid colours—reds and greens, and yellows, and blue the shade of her eyes. He wanted to see her dressed in them and in stylish clothes. Properly clothed, he was certain, she would be a most striking woman. Jason knew that she would reject any offer from him of so much as one gown. He would have to think of another way to provide them for her.

But why should he want to do so? In vain he told himself it was out of gratitude for transforming his sister into a talkative, curious young lady. He was actually becoming fond of the chit. But, to his genuine amazement, he realised that he was becoming even fonder of Anna. After all these years he had at last met a female whom he not only liked but felt instinctively that he could trust. He wanted so much to believe that in Anna he had, at last, found a woman who would never deceive him, but he could not bear to be disillusioned again.

CHAPTER THIRTEEN

ANNABELLE, Jason, and his sister concluded their sight-seeing in Rouen with a visit to St Maclou's, a fifteenth-century church in the Flamboyant Gothic style. As they left it to make their way back to their *diligence*, Ellerton suddenly asked in that abrupt way of his, 'Have you spent much time in London, Miss Smith?'

'Not for several years,' Annabelle answered, uneasy with any conversation that involved her past. 'My papa preferred the country.' She did not disclose that the country her father had preferred was in the West Indies.

'Did you have a come-out Season, Miss Smith?' Jason asked.

'Yes, when I was eighteen.'

'You were not a success?'

Unwilling to lie, Annabelle parried the question by saying lightly, 'I am on the shelf, am I not?'

'Did you have no offers at all?'

By now Annabelle had learned that such blunt questions were spurred only by Ellerton's curiosity and that he was not being intentionally uncivil in asking them. 'It does not signify,' she replied. 'Nor have you any right to ask such a question.'

'No, I don't,' Jason agreed amiably.

Annabelle, uncomfortable with the conversation, turned to talk to Rachel, only to discover that the girl had stopped some distance back to turn and again admire St Maclou's lovely west front.

'I do not recall hearing of you in London,' Jason said musingly to Annabelle.

'You would be the first to tell me that I am not a memorable woman,' she retorted, two red spots of colour suddenly shining on her cheeks. His comments on Lady Belle were not nearly so forgettable to her as he had found the lady herself to be.

'I am neither so uncivil nor so dishonest as to tell you that,' he protested.

Annabelle bit back the retort that he had already told her precisely that. Instead, suspecting him of craven flattery although to what purpose she could not fathom, she said, 'You waste your gallantry on me.'

'Believe me,' he replied in nettled accents, 'I never pay false compliments. Did we ever meet back when you were on the town?'

'No, we did not. You were not the sort of man that an innocent young girl, steeped in the proprieties, was permitted to know.' She could not resist adding in amusement, 'Although we never met, your reputation was well known to me even then.'

'What is his reputation, Anna?' Rachel interjected, wide-eyed. Neither Jason nor the governess had heard her come up behind them as they were talking.

Annabelle had no desire to enlighten the innocent girl about the Notorious Marquess, and she said hastily, 'He is reputed to—ah—to be quite charming when he wishes to be.'

'Jason is never charming,' Rachel assured her.

'Thank you, dear sister, for your kind defence of me.'

Rachel looked terrified until she noticed the laughter in Jason's silver-grey eyes.

'Are you funning me again?' she asked, nervously hopeful.

'Yes, puss, I am,' he assured her.

Rachel rewarded him with such an intense look of relief that he was startled.

In the days that followed, as they travelled south towards Paris from Rouen, the weather grew progressively hotter and more sultry.

Annabelle, sweltering in the heavy black material of her hand-me-down gown, would have given anything to be able to change it for a lighter one, like the pretty white muslin that Rachel was wearing, if only she had one with her.

'You must be suffocating in that dress,' the Marquess observed with his customary abruptness.

'One must make do with what one has,' she told him lightly.

The following day Annabelle was startled to discover that the closed *diligence de ville* they had been using had been replaced with a landau, its folding head, which divided in the middle, neatly collapsed behind each of the facing seats.

'Why the change?' Annabelle asked the Marquess as he handed her into the new vehicle.

'I am persuaded that you will find this cooler,' he replied as he climbed in after her and took the opposite seat.

And he was right. Although the day was hot and still, the rapid pace of the hired team generated a blessed breeze. Annabelle was touched by Lord Ellerton's concern for her comfort.

She was also startled by how seriously a man of his reputation took his familial obligations. She had learned that he had come to France to try to rescue his French relatives from financial ruin. His mother had been the daughter of the Duc de Thury. Both her father and his heir, her brother, had been beheaded during the Terror, and all of the family's properties looted and seized. Her brother's wife, Claudine, had escaped with her life. So had her only son, who had subsequently married and produced two sons of his own. Now both he and his wife were dead, and Claudine, virtually destitute, was raising her two grandsons, aged nineteen and seventeen, alone.

Jason hoped to recover enough of the family's assets so that with careful management and investment they might at least live comfortably. He confessed to Annabelle that he felt a double responsibility towards Claudine because, in addition to being his uncle's widow, she had been his mother's childhood best friend.

The better Annabelle came to know her employer, the more guilty she felt about having deceived him about her identity. She was haunted by the fear that she might be recognised with him; thereby embroiling him in a dreadful scandal. When she had conceived her scheme, she had felt that, if this should happen, it was no more than such a dishonourable man deserved. She knew now that she had been seriously misled about his character, and with each passing day her uneasiness and guilt over her deceit increased.

As they neared the end of their journey and the domes and spires of Paris came into view on the horizon, Annabelle, who was seated with her back to the horses, was so excited that she craned her neck in a most unladylike manner trying to get a better look at the city that she had so long dreamed of visiting.

The Marquess ordered the landau stopped and insisted that Annabelle exchange seats with him so that she could more easily see the city as they approached it.

She protested, 'But you will not be able to see Paris.'

'But I saw it when I was a boy, and you have never seen it,' he said firmly, settling himself on the seat that she had been occupying. There was an odd light in his grey eyes as he said, 'I find the view from this position quite interesting, too.'

Annabelle, unconscious of the excitement that animated her face and the happy glow in her eyes, looked at him as if he had taken leave of his senses, for all he had to see was a road lined with dilapidated buildings. They were distinctly uninteresting, housing what seemed to her like an inordinate number of *guinguettes* the small public houses where artisans and labourers gathered for refreshment and dancing.

A few minutes later Jason pointed out the mismatched towers of the Abbey St Denis that had been the mausoleum of France's kings. During the Revolution, the mob had attacked it, stripping its altar and choir and disinterring royal remains.

Annabelle shuddered as she remembered the awful story her cousin Jean-Louis had told her about the mob, lacking any respect for the dead, using King Henry IV's skull as a football.

The road grew increasingly crowded with conveyances that ranged from handsome *diligences* to broken down farmers' carts. By the time their landau passed through the Porte St Denis, the massive triumphant arch extolling Louis XIV's battlefield victories, it had been forced to slow to a crawl.

But Annabelle did not mind. She eagerly took in every detail as they rode along an impressively wide boulevard lined with great houses, heavily embellished with friezes, cornices, pillars, pilasters, and balconies. Each side of the broad avenue was lined with towering plane trees whose spreading limbs shaded the landau from the hot afternoon sun. Between the rows of trees and the houses, pedestrians strolled along broad gravelled walks, protected from the dangers of horse-drawn vehicles.

When Annabelle voiced her approval of these pleasant pedestrian lanes, the Marquess said, 'Paris is a city to be explored on foot: the boulevards, the quays, the gardens. I know of no more interesting city to walk in.'

'There is so much I want to see,' Annabelle confided, her face glowing with excitement.

'What tops your list?' Jason asked. 'The Louvre?'

'No, although naturally I want to see it, but most of all I want to visit the Jardin des Plantes,' replied Annabelle, who had shared her father's fascination with botany.

'What an unusual choice, but then I have come to expect the unusual from you,' Jason observed. 'I am relieved that the city appears to have been little damaged when the allies occupied it. It would have been a wretched crime if they had bombarded it to rubble.'

Rachel, less interested in recent history than in her future comfort, asked, 'Where shall we stay while we are here?'

'I have taken a *hôtel* off the Rue Royale near the Place Louis Quinze,' Jason told her.

Annabelle's pulse quickened. The *hôtel* of the Comte de Vergennes, if it still belonged to Jean-Louis, was located not far away on the Place Vendôme. As soon as she could slip away, she would go there to enquire about him.

'You have taken an entire hotel?' Rachel asked in surprise.

Her brother laughed. 'Yes, but *hôtel* has a different meaning in Paris. Large private houses are called *hôtels* because sometimes they are divided up and portions of them let.'

The landau turned down a narrow street lined with houses as massive and grandly ornamented as those on the broad boulevard had been. From a distance they were an impressive sight, but up close Annabelle saw that their courtyards were often dirty, and the people who hurried in and out of their great doors ill-dressed.

'What impresses you the most thus far about Paris?' Jason asked Annabelle.

'The contrasts,' she replied promptly. 'The houses are so grand in size and exterior ornament. They must be twice the height of London dwellings, and so elaborate with all those cornices and friezes and pilasters and balconies. Yet they are often ill-kept, with dirty, littered courtyards.'

Jason smiled. 'I am assured that our *hôtel* is in excellent repair.'

He had not been misled, they discovered, when the landau stopped in front of a classically elegant stone mansion, rising five storeys, its top floor tucked into a mansard roof. The residence was so large that Annabelle could not refrain from asking him teasingly whether he did not think it much too small for them.

He grinned. 'Yes, indeed, but we shall have to make do.'

Rachel, who had taken this exchange seriously, asked in wonderment, 'How can you possibly think it is too small?'

'Miss Smith was quizzing me, puss,' her brother explained, 'and I responded in kind.'

'Oh,' Rachel said in a small voice, wide-eyed at the thought that anyone would dare to tease her intimidating brother.

The interior of the *hôtel* was as elegant as the exterior, although Jason looked with disfavour upon the delicate French Louis XV furnishings, especially the small chairs *à l'Artois*, that were expected to accommodate his large frame.

Once Annabelle was settled in her new quarters, she tried to slip out to find the Place Vendôme and Jean-Louis's hotel. But Jason saw her leaving and insisted on squiring her on an introductory stroll.

'But you cannot be seen with me,' she protested, trying to dissuade him from accompanying her. 'Only think of what it will do to your reputation.'

'*My* reputation?' the Notorious Marquess enquired.

'Yes, yours,' she replied gravely. 'It will be sadly lowered if you are recognised with such a plain creature as myself on your arm rather than one of your gorgeous demi-reps.'

He laughed. 'In that case, I consider it woefully in need of lowering. Shall we go?'

He gave her his arm, and she had no choice but to take it.

As they walked down the Rue Royale, Annabelle could not help but look a little enviously at the stylishly dressed women she saw promenading there. She had never felt so dowdy and unfashionable in Tante Marie's cast-off as she did now on Jason's arm, but she did not refine upon why she would have so liked to have him be proud of her.

After a while the Rue Royale broadened into an enormous square. Off it to the left, a broad gravel alley led through lovely gardens decorated with fountains, statues, and urns to a large palace beyond. To the right lay the broadest, most impressive avenue that Annabelle had yet seen in Paris—or anywhere, for that matter. In front of her, beyond a handsome bridge spanning the River Seine, was another palace with a classic Greek portico, and near it the great gilded dome that she recognised as belonging to the Invalides.

'Beautiful, is it not?' Jason observed. 'The gardens on your left are the Tuileries with the palace beyond. The broad avenue on your right is the Champs-Élysées, and across the river is the Palais-Bourbon.'

'What is this square called?'

'Place Louis Quinze.'

The pleasure vanished from Annabelle's face. 'Oh, no!' she gasped, the horrors that had occurred on this lovely spot casting a pall on her appreciation of its beauty. She was standing in the very place where poor Tante Marie's husband and so many other victims of the Terror had been guillotined.

'You are suddenly very pale,' Jason observed in concern. 'Are you ill?'

Annabelle dared not tell him that a relative had been beheaded here, for Jason would want to know who he was. Instead, she said, 'I was thinking of all the poor people, even the King and Queen, who died here.

'I know,' Jason said, his voice suddenly husky. 'It is where my grandfather and uncle died.'

Later Annabelle persuaded him to take her to the Place Vendôme on the pretext that she wanted to see the great pillar, an imitation of the Trajan column at Rome, that Napoleon had raised there in his own honour. Her real purpose, however, was to locate her cousin's *hôtel*.

When they reached the square, the buildings surrounding it looked exactly as Jean-Louis had described them to Annabelle all those years ago at Hillbrook: the arcades at ground level, the tall Corinthian pilasters, the mansard roofs with dormer windows, even the faces carved into the keystones over the arches of the arcades.

Only the monument in the centre of the square was different. The huge equestrian statue of Louis XIV that Jean-Louis had described had been destroyed during the Revolution. In its place, enclosed by an iron railing, stood a bronze shaft soaring one hundred and forty feet high.

Staring up at the top of the column, where a white flag waved from a pole, Jason said drily, 'Napoleon did not believe in leaving it to history to honour him, did he?'

'Perhaps he feared it would not do so,' Annabelle said tartly.

'I understand that there was a statue of the little corporal where the white flag now flies. Perhaps the entire column will eventually disappear as the previous monument to the Sun King did.'

'I hope so,' Annabelle said, full of hostility for the man who had been her nation's arch-enemy.

She looked eagerly around the square until she located her cousin's former—and perhaps present— home. She had to restrain herself from running to it. Instead, trying to keep her tone casual, she said, 'The Comte de Vergennes had a *hôtel* here on the Place Vendôme. I wonder if he still lives here.'

Jason looked at her sharply. 'How do you know him?'

'I met him at Hillbrook; the late Earl of Chilton was his uncle and gave him refuge from the Terror there,' Annabelle replied, wondering why Jason's silver-grey eyes were suddenly so suspicious. Nervously, she hurried on. 'The Comte returned to France when Napoleon crowned himself Emperor. I have heard nothing more of him since, and I have often wondered what fate he met upon his return here.' She gestured towards the building that she had picked out. 'I believe that is his *hôtel*.'

Jason suddenly looked so forbidding that Annabelle was disconcerted. He said coldly, 'Clearly the Comte made a remarkable impression upon you, if you still remember both him and his Paris address so well.'

'He was a charming man,' Annabelle said hastily. Her good sense warned her not to press the issue in light of Jason's peculiar reaction, but she had waited too long to learn Jean-Louis's fate. She could not turn away when the answer—and her cousin himself—might be only a few yards away. 'Perhaps we could enquire whether the Comte still lives there or, indeed, if he is still alive.'

'Yes, we can enquire.' Jason's voice was at its most sardonic. 'But I doubt that you will find him there. From its run-down appearance, I would wager that it has been carved up into small apartments that are let cheaply.'

Jason was proven correct. A wizened old hag with most of her teeth missing seemed to be in charge of the building. She offered to rent them a portion of the first floor for six hundred francs. When they declined this, she offered them an attic for forty francs.

When Annabelle asked about the Comte de Vergennes, the woman's seamed face saddened, and two tears welled up in eyes that were milky from cataracts. 'The dear Comte, he is dead.'

Annabelle reeled back at this information and had to put her hand against the wall to steady herself.

'Are you certain?' she gasped, drawing a probing look from Jason.

'*Mais oui,*' the old woman replied firmly.

Although Annabelle had known that Jean-Louis might be dead, she had been confident that he was still alive and that she would find him. A wave of despair overwhelmed her, and only Jason's eyes, as hard and glittering as diamonds, studying her stopped her from bursting into tears for her dead cousin.

Annabelle, still too stunned by the news that Jean-Louis was dead to speak, allowed Jason to lead her away from the *hôtel*. As they walked back towards their lodging in silence, she wondered what she could do now. With her cousin dead, her trip to France had been in vain. Now there was no one to help her against her brother's despotism.

CHAPTER FOURTEEN

AFTER Annabelle and Jason returned from the Place Vendôme, he left almost immediately to call on his aunt and her grandsons. She retired to her room on the pretext of suffering from a headache and wept for Jean-Louis. Having no appetite, she refused dinner and was still awake with her grief when Jason came in long past midnight from his visit with his relatives.

Finally, Annabelle fell into a fitful sleep. When she arose the next morning her eyes were still swollen and red from crying. She dreaded facing Jason's probing gaze, and she postponed going downstairs, remaining in her room until she thought he would have left.

Although she had known before she set out for France that her cousin might be dead, she had told herself fiercely that he had to be alive and that eventually she would find him. Now that the first shock of learning of his death was wearing off, she had to address the pressing question of what she herself should do. Should she try to remain in France or plan to go back to England when the Marquess did and look for employment there? Annabelle was certain of only one thing. She would not return to her brother's house. She would prefer to be an abigail or even a scullery maid! But surely she would think of a better solution during the weeks that Lord Ellerton would be in France.

When she finally came downstairs, she discovered that she had been a few minutes premature. Jason had not yet left but was in the hall, pulling on his gloves preparatory to departing. He frowned when he saw her. 'You look as though you had a dreadful night,' he observed in that blunt manner of his.

He did, too. His grey eyes had never looked so tired to her, and the harsh lines of his face were more deeply etched than usual. Without thinking, Annabelle said, 'So do you.'

'Yes, I had some unpleasant things to contemplate,' he replied enigmatically.

'Your relatives' affairs?'

'Among other things. They are in worse order than I had been led to believe. I am on my way to Tante Claudine's now.'

He examined Annabelle so searchingly that she was again acutely conscious of how shabby she looked in her black bombazine dress that was far too heavy for the warmth of the day.

'You need lighter clothes for this climate,' he said with his habitual curtness. 'I am having a modiste that Tante Claudine recommended call on Rachel today. While the woman is here, have her make you a gown or two as well. I am told her prices are very reasonable. I shall subtract the cost of the gowns from your salary.'

Without waiting for Annabelle's response, he turned and hurried out of the door.

Not that she would have argued with him. She would welcome a gown of lighter material and more recent style.

When the modiste, a Madame St Avant, arrived, Annabelle was impressed by the woman's talent as evidenced by her sketches. Rachel quickly ordered several gowns, but Annabelle had to be more careful. She selected two simple muslins, one in a bright yellow, and the other in a blue that matched her eyes. How wonderful it would be to wear colours again now that her mourning period for her father was ending. Annabelle detested black and knew that she looked dreadful in it besides.

When she learned the reasonable cost of the two designs she had selected, she was sorely tempted to order a third, but she restrained herself.

Madame St Avant, complimenting Annabelle on her taste, professed herself eager to have mademoiselle's opinion on various colours, fabrics, accessories, and on a number of other designs of more elaborate gowns.

'Which do you like the best?' the modiste pressed after she had spread out the sketches for Annabelle's viewing.

'In truth, I cannot decide among these four.' Annabelle pointed to her selections. 'They are all so beautiful.'

When her father was alive, she would have ordered all four without a second's hesitation. Those days were gone forever, but Annabelle wasted no time on self-pity. She would make the best of whatever hand life dealt her rather than crying over it, which accomplished nothing.

Annabelle saw nothing more of Jason the remainder of that day or the next, so busy was he trying to set to right the affairs of his aunt and her grandsons. Having become accustomed to his company on the journey to Paris, Annabelle discovered that she sorely missed it when it was withdrawn. Even Rachel admitted that their dinners were not so interesting with him gone.

In his absence Rachel pleaded in vain with her governess to take her to the Louvre. On the third day it occurred to Annabelle that she was unconsciously trying to postpone the visit until Jason might be free to accompany them.

'Perhaps your brother would like to go,' she said to Rachel.

'Oh, no!' the girl assured her earnestly. 'When he agreed, much against his will, to bring me to Paris, he specifically warned me that I was never to plague him to take me places like the Louvre.'

Since Jason would not be interested anyway, Annabelle capitulated and took Rachel. When they came home in late afternoon, they discovered that he had returned early for the first time in three days and was waiting for them.

'Where have you been,' he demanded irritably. 'I wanted to take you to the Louvre this afternoon.'

'That is where we were,' Rachel said blithely.

He was clearly disappointed. 'I had hoped to take you.'

'But,' Rachel said in confusion, 'you told me never to plague you to take me there. I thought that you did not want to see it.'

'I have had a change of heart since London, puss,' he replied. 'Nor can I permit you to wander about Paris unescorted. I will set aside some time each afternoon to take you out.'

'But I am not unescorted; I have Anna,' retorted Rachel, who was not overly eager for her brother's company. Although she no longer thought him to be the monster that she had before Annabelle had come, she still regarded him with considerable awe and trepidation.

'I said I would escort you,' he said with a finality that discouraged his sister from further protest.

Later, when Rachel was not with them, Annabelle asked Jason whether he insisted upon accompanying them because he did not trust her to keep his sister out of mischief.

'Don't be a peabrain. You can handle her better than anyone alive.' There was a warmth in his silver eyes that made her heart skip erratically. 'I trust you as I have never trusted another woman and, coming from me, that is a high compliment.'

But not one that she deserved, Annabelle thought guiltily, her happiness dissolving. 'Why do you distrust my sex so much?'

The warmth vanished from Jason's eyes. 'It has given me good reason to do so,' he snapped, abruptly turning away from her.

And she, dear God, was giving him additional reason by deceiving him about her true identity.

How she wished now that she had not brushed aside Claire's concerns so cavalierly. The better Annabelle came to know the Marquess, the more certain she was that he would never forgive her should he learn what she had done.

In the weeks that followed, Jason was true to his word, returning home by mid-afternoon to introduce Rachel and Annabelle to some new aspect of Paris from the Jardin des Plantes to the Pantheon.

Their days fell into a pattern. Annabelle and Rachel would devote the mornings to her lessons and the afternoons to exploring Paris with Jason. At night the three of them would dine together at home.

These meals were punctuated with lively arguments between Annabelle and Jason, often prompted by one or the other of them being deliberately provocative. Dinner was Annabelle's favourite time with him. They often became so engrossed in their wide-ranging discussions they lingered for hours at the table.

Rachel listened in amazement as her brave governess argued vigorously with her fearsome brother on a wide variety of subjects. Even more astonishing to the girl was the realisation that Jason, rather than being angered by Anna's daring to contradict him, clearly enjoyed this verbal sparring.

Before Anna, Rachel had known women only like her mother and aunt, whose conversations, devoted to ailments, complaints, and gossip, had bored her excessively. But Anna was so different, and Rachel decided that she wanted nothing so much as to be like her. Soon the girl was applying herself to her lessons with a diligence that would have confounded her long line of former governesses.

One afternoon they climbed the three hundred and eighty-nine steps to the top of one of the Cathedral of Notre-Dame's twin towers for the spectacular view of Paris that it afforded. As they looked out over the city with its tree-lined avenues and its elegant architecture, Jason said mockingly, 'I collect, Anna, that heights bother you no more than rough seas or highwaymen do.'

She stiffened at his use of her given name, remembering how he had deliberately used it as an insult during the interview in London. 'No, *Jason*, they do not bother me.'

He grinned at her. 'I like the way you say my name. I hope you will continue to call me by it.'

'It would be most improper,' she said, startled. 'I am your sister's governess.'

'But you know how improper I am. In fact, I insist that you call me Jason hereafter.'

'I cannot,' she protested, strongly suspecting that he had deliberately provoked her into doing so just then.

'I am your employer, and I have the right to insist upon you calling me what I wish,' he said with a grin.

Annabelle was struck by how handsome his dark face was when the harsh lines relaxed in a smile.

'Has anyone ever told you what a fascinating voice you have, Anna,' he asked.

Seeing her shock, he raised a mocking eyebrow. 'Don't worry, I am not trying to seduce you. I merely like your voice.'

Annabelle suddenly felt irrationally cross that he had not enough interest in her to think of seducing her. Good Lord, she wondered in shock, was she losing her mind? No, she thought wryly, more likely her heart. To cover her confusion, she began hastily, 'Lord Ellerton, I——'

'Anna,' he interrupted reprovingly. 'I told you to call me Jason.'

'Odious creature!' she exclaimed, defeated.

It was two weeks before the clothes that had been ordered from Madame St Avant arrived.

Opening the boxes designated for her, Annabelle discovered that they contained in addition to the two simple muslins that she had ordered, the four far more elaborate gowns whose sketches she had admired, as well as matching shoes, shawls, fans, and other accessories.

Annabelle stared at the clothes in horrified disbelief. How outraged Jason must have been at the size of the bill for all this finery she had not ordered.

She rushed off in search of him. Finding him in his office poring over more of his relatives' financial documents, she burst in, much agitated. 'When you received the bill from Madame St Avant, you must have been shocked at how wretchedly extravagant I seemed, but——'

He looked up with a smile at her entrance. 'Yes, I was shocked, but only by how modest the bill was.'

A dark suspicion flashed through her mind as she looked into his inscrutable silver eyes. 'I cannot let you pay for my clothes,' she protested. 'It would be most improper.'

'Indeed, it would be,' he agreed, 'and I have subtracted the amount, as I said I would, from your salary.'

'I fear that I would have to work for you until Rachel's children are grown to pay off Madame St Avant's bill.'

'Then clearly I am too niggardly in the salary I pay you,' Jason said, an amused twinkle in his eye. 'Are you requesting an increase in your salary?'

'Do be serious!'

'I am, and this is much ado about nothing.' He rummaged through the papers on his desk and, extracting one, handed it to her. 'Here is the bill.'

She took it from him. The total, written in an ornate hand, was for two gowns at the price that Madame had quoted her.

'You see, the cost of the clothes that you ordered was quite modest,' Jason said.

'What about the cost of the clothes that I did not order? I repeat, I cannot permit you to dress me.'

'But I am not,' he said blandly. 'The other things are not from me. They are a present from Rachel.

There is nothing improper about accepting a gift from your pupil. Indeed, you would sadly wound her feelings if you were not to do so.'

'Yes, you would,' said Rachel, who had slipped into the room behind Annabelle.

Rachel proved as stubborn as her brother on the subject. Annabelle was put in the unhappy position of either accepting the clothes or seeming to be extremely ungrateful, and she capitulated. Madame St Avant's prices were so reasonable and her clothes of such superior quality and style that they were an enormous bargain.

Several times Jason's relatives came to dine with them. His Tante Claudine was a short, plump woman whose large dark eyes contrasted vividly with the snowy white of her hair. She was a cheerful woman who had not been embittered by the tragedies that life had dealt her, and Annabelle liked her very much.

Claudine's young grandsons, Ambroise and Georges, were slim and darkly handsome with their grandmother's black eyes and pleasant disposition. Rachel was immediately infatuated with Georges, while Ambroise developed a tendre for Annabelle, much to her amusement.

Jason was less amused. 'Does the puppy annoy you?' he asked her one night after his cousin had regarded her with particularly adoring eyes.

She laughed. 'To the contrary, I find it flattering that he would even notice a hag so long in the tooth as myself.'

The explorations of Paris continued, and sometimes Ambroise and Georges accompanied them. Jason was amenable to taking Annabelle and Rachel wherever they wished to go except to the Palais-Royal. He explained to the governess that he did not think it a proper place to take a girl as young as his sister, but he promised that he would escort Annabelle there, if she wished, when his aunt took Rachel on a forthcoming outing to the country.

One day the Marquess, his sister, and Annabelle explored the stalls along the Boulevard des Italiens, where flower girls and fruit women urged their wares. The smell of roasted chestnuts permeated the air.

So did the music of a one-man band, an old greybeard who managed to play simultaneously a harp, flute, drum, and triangle while his foot moved a small wooden scaramouch that danced in time to its busy master's music.

'The old man reminds me of myself trying to straighten out my relatives' affairs,' Jason said humorously.

Annabelle knew how hard he had been working on them. Half of his days and additional hours late at night were devoted to them. From one of her windows she could look across the courtyard to the ground-floor room that he used as an office. The summer nights were hot, and he opened the French doors wide. Often, after she and Rachel retired, he would return to the office, and she would see him through those open doors, sitting at his desk, poring over papers in front of him. Annabelle had been more than a little amazed at how dedicated Jason was to helping his relatives. Not many men would have regarded them as their responsibility as he clearly did.

'Are your efforts on their behalf succeeding?' she asked him sympathetically.

'Yes, but I fear it will take longer than I antici-pated. Will you mind a few additional weeks in Paris?'

Mind! Annabelle thought joyfully. She had de-cided that she should remain in Paris when he left, and she suddenly felt as if she had won a reprieve from the guillotine to be able to spend more time with him before she must make her own way among strangers in a strange land.

Farther along the boulevard, Annabelle and her two companions stopped to listen to the lovely, sultry voices of two female ballad singers per-forming on a street corner for the scanty coins of passers-by. They held themselves proudly, but they had wrapped themselves in worn veils that fell to their feet in a pathetic attempt to protect their anonymity. Annabelle knew that if their identities became known, their reputations would be as tat-tered as their veils.

These singers and their veils spoke silently but eloquently of the difficulty that women alone and without money had in eking out a living. It was a difficulty that Annabelle would soon share.

Another day, as she strolled with Jason and his sister along the quays on the River Seine among pedlars hawking birds in cages and little trees in pots, Annabelle stopped to stare down at the water, where the washerwomen of Paris in their white caps and richly coloured handkerchiefs scrubbed linens through latticelike openings in large rafts.

The sight depressed her spirits, and she wondered whether, if she remained in France, she might be forced to join their ranks. The thought of what her life in France would be like once Jason left threatened to bring tears to her eyes. Suddenly it came to her that any future which did not include him would be bleak. Silently, she berated herself for having been such a corkbrain as to have fallen in love with the Notorious Marquess. She must be a trifle off her hinges to have lost her heart to a man who had none when it came to the women he romanced.

His treatment of Lord Ivly's daughter seriously disturbed Annabelle. She could neither justify nor understand his reprehensible behaviour in that instance, especially when in every other he exhibited such a strong sense of familial duty.

Nevertheless, Annabelle was hopelessly, irrevocably in love with Jason. She wondered whether he would be amused or furious to learn that his sister's governess had lost her heart to him. Probably a little of both, she thought.

With each passing day her guilt over having deceived him about her identity intensified. Her only solace was that she had helped bring about a reconciliation between him and his sister. Once he had understood the reason for Rachel's maddening behaviour, he had worked hard to put her at her ease with him. Not only had the girl lost her fear of him by now, but a strong mutual affection was blooming between them.

Annabelle was amazed that a man with the Notorious Marquess's much-publicised predilection for the muslin company was content to dine quietly at home with her and his sister night after night, abstaining from all the scandalous entertainments that Paris offered. One evening she taxed him about this.

He looked at her oddly for a long moment, as though he were about to say something and then thought better of it. When he answered, it was with a self-deprecatory smile, 'I am not quite so black as the world paints me.' His harsh face grew serious. 'The truth is I have been leading a very quiet life since Rachel came to live with me. I want no hint of scandal to attach to her name nor to mine while she is in my custody. I will not take the smallest chance that I might jeopardise the kind of marriage my father wished for her.'

His words struck terror in Annabelle's heart as she recalled Claire's warning about the scandal that would erupt should it ever be learned that Lady Belle Smythe had accompanied Lord Ellerton to France disguised as his half-sister's governess.

Annabelle had thought that the Notorious Marquess would not care a snap, but now she knew that he would care very much. Worse, if she were recognised living under his protection, he would find himself, through no fault of his own, hopelessly embroiled in a scandal that could rival even his affair with Lord Ivly's daughter.

Annabelle uttered a prayer of thanksgiving that they were in France, where no one knew her.

CHAPTER FIFTEEN

ON THE day that Rachel went on her outing to the country with Tante Claudine, Jason had an important appointment in the morning on behalf of his aunt and her grandsons that prevented him from taking Annabelle to the Palais-Royal until the afternoon.

Annabelle dressed with particular care in one of Madame St Avant's lovely creations of vivid red tissue silk. She realised with wry amusement that she was as excited at the prospect of spending the afternoon with Jason as a schoolroom miss before her first ball.

He had been obliged to dine at the British ambassador's the previous night. It had been the first time in weeks that he had not been home for dinner, and the meal devoid of his company had been dull. If Annabelle missed him so dreadfully when he was gone for one night, how miserable her life would be when he was gone from it forever.

As Annabelle left her room, she caught a glimpse of herself in a long gilt-framed mirror that hung by the door. She was startled at how little she resembled the dowdy creature who had come to France with Jason and at how much like the vivacious Lady Belle of old she looked.

The Palais-Royal was not far from their hotel, and Annabelle, who loved strolling along the streets of Paris, told Jason that she preferred to walk to it.

As they did so, she asked him how his important appointment had gone that morning.

'So well that I think it will not be long now before we will be able to return home.'

She wondered whom the appointment could have been with that it had been so effective, but, since Jason did not volunteer this information, she did not enquire.

The Palais-Royal was a study in contrasts, simultaneously beautiful and ugly. Annabelle stood in the large interior square formed on three sides by splendid and imposing stone buildings that included the original palace built by Cardinal Richelieu and the additions by Philippe II of Orleans, the notorious regent for a young Louis XV, and the Duc's descendant, Philippe Égalité. On the fourth side of the garden, however, wretched wooden barracks sadly detracted from the elegant effect.

Jason guided Annabelle through one of the arches, separated by Corinthian pilasters, on to the arcade lined with shops as exclusive and expensive as any in London's Bond Street. They strode past silversmiths and perfumers, drapers and toymakers. At a clock shop they stopped to admire a handsome timepiece in a case of whitest alabaster.

As they stepped out of the shop on to the arcade crowded with people, Annabelle said, 'Now I know why you did not wish to bring Rachel here. You feared she would see so much that she wanted that you would be swept into River Tick.'

He laughed. 'Rachel is not that expensive! I did not wish to bring her because behind this beautiful façade the *palais* has its ugly side. There are less savoury wares peddled behind these elegant shops.'

She gained some illumination of this a few minutes later when she happened past a bookstore tucked away off the main arcade. Idly picking up a volume on a table in front of it, she opened to an illustration and gasped in shock as she realised what was depicted in it.

'I collect your meaning now,' she said, hastily closing the book.

Jason took the volume from her hands and laid it back on the table. 'How pretty you are when you blush,' he observed softly, and chuckled as his words brought an even rosier hue to her cheeks.

Leading her back to the main arcade, he said, 'The Palais-Royal has considerably more scandalous offerings than that book. There are some infamous bawdy houses and gaming hells tucked away here, too.'

'That seems only fitting in light of the orgies that went on here when it was the home of the dissolute regent.' Seeing Jason's startled expression, she enquired, 'Has my frank tongue shocked you?'

'No, only surprised me. But I do not know why it should have. Your plain speaking is one of the things I most like about you.' He gave her a warm, glowing smile that would have melted her heart had he not already melted it long ago. 'How pretty you look today. France has agreed with you. You have bloomed since you have been here.'

The sincerity of his words was underscored by the admiration in his eyes, and Annabelle suddenly felt like the most beautiful woman on earth. A choking lump rose in her throat at the thought of remaining behind when he returned to England and never seeing him again. The prospect of her life, once he was gone permanently from it, seemed a parched desert to her. But she well knew that there was no hope, no future for her and Jason. She had foreclosed it when first she had deceived him. He would not look at her approvingly were he to learn of her deceit.

'What is wrong, Anna?' Jason asked, his suddenly soft voice a caress.

'I . . . I was thinking how much I love . . . France,' she lied, quickly changing the subject. 'Did you enjoy the ambassador's dinner last night?'

'No, it was exceedingly tedious. There are more English aristocrats in Paris than there are in London.'

'Truly?' Annabelle asked in alarm.

'Truly. It shouldn't surprise me if we ran into one or two of them here today.'

Annabelle, paling, hastily looked about her, terrified she would see a familiar face that would recognise her and expose her masquerade. She remembered with chagrin her blithe assurance to Claire that she would be in a strange land where no one would know her. Yes, she was in a foreign land, but now, it would appear, so were a good many of her countrymen who might know her.

'I fear a change of geography fails to make some Englishmen any more interesting,' Jason said, 'particularly that gossiping bore, Lord Rudolph Oldfield. He was so full of the latest scandal to rock London what he could talk of nothing else.'

'What scandal?' Annabelle asked idly. 'Has Prinny developed a passionate tendre for another grandmotherly lady?'

'No. In fact, you might find it of interest since it involves your former neighbour, Lady Belle Smythe.'

'Lady Belle?' Annabelle echoed faintly.

'Yes, she has eloped with a secret lover.'

'What!' Annabelle gasped, stopping dead before the windows of the Égalité Coffee House, oblivious to the noise of arguing voices drifting out through the shop's open door. 'But that is nonsense! I . . . she would not do such a ramshackle thing.'

'Apparently, you do not know her as well as you think.'

Annabelle bit back a retort that no one knew her better, and settled instead for protesting, 'It is a slander.'

'Oh, no, it is quite true,' Jason assured her. 'Her own brother has broadcast it all over London. Why would he tarnish his family's name if it were not true?'

Why, indeed? Annabelle wondered in horrified bewilderment. Surely Frederick must know that it would ruin her. Did he hate her so much? Annabelle was so stunned that it was a full minute before she could regain her voice. When she did so, it mirrored her confusion. 'I don't understand. Why would Chilton want to spread such a dreadful story about his own sister? Even if it were true, and I am confident that it is not, one would think that he would want to keep such folly a secret.'

A sneer twisted Jason's face. He looked so contemptuous that Annabelle was unnerved. 'It is absolutely clear what his game is.'

'It is?' Annabelle said faintly. 'I fear it is not at all clear to me.'

'Chilton and his conniving sister are obviously conspiring to force her lover, whoever the poor fool is, into marrying her.'

'How can you think such a thing!' Annabelle cried, horrified.

'Clearly her lover had no intention of marrying her, or he would have done so. When she could not get him to throw the handkerchief, she and her brother devised this little scheme to force him into parson's mousetrap.'

Stung by Jason's reasoning, which Annabelle knew was distorted by his contemptuous opinion of women, she demanded, 'Why should Lady Belle resort to such tactics when you yourself said that she turned down several very advantageous offers.'

'That was when she was young and foolishly overestimated her charm,' Jason said cuttingly.

They were still standing in front of the Égalité Coffee House, where Annabelle had stopped so abruptly, and by now passers-by were beginning to stare at them.

'You are very much mistaken about Lady Belle!' she protested.

Jason cocked a cynical eyebrow. 'You don't believe that is her game?'

'I would as soon believe it of myself! Lady Belle would never seek to trap an unwilling man. She was never eager to marry.'

'Nor will she ever again have the opportunity if she and her odious brother fail in this scheme,' Jason said grimly. 'If her lover withstands the pressure to marry her, she will be beyond the pale. Only the most egregious fortune hunter would wed her then.'

Which Annabelle knew was true, but she was too distressed at Jason's unjust reading of Lady Belle's character to dwell upon the fatal damage that her brother had inflicted on her reputation. 'How can you speak with such certainty about Lady Belle when you have never met her?' she cried.

'I do not need to meet her to know what she is like! I have already met too many deceitful women like her.' The bitterness in Jason's voice seemed to come from the very depths of his soul.

But Annabelle was too deeply wounded by his contemptuous assessment of Lady Belle to refine upon it. Remembering his shabby treatment of Lord Ivly's daughter, she cried angrily, 'How cynical you are about women when, given your history, it is women who should be cynical of you!'

Jason's face took on the appearance of a thundercloud. It was clear that he knew what she was referring to, and he looked as though he had been goaded beyond endurance. He said nothing, but it was a minute before he regained sufficient control that he could say through clenched teeth, 'Let us go!' He took her arm and led her at a rapid pace to the exit.

Through the window of the Égalité Coffee House a portly exquisite, overdressed and overfed, watched with undisguised glee as Jason hurried Annabelle away.

Lord Rudolph Oldfield had chosen a table that offered him a view of the crowded piazza. He was leaving for England on the morrow, and he had come to the Palais-Royal in search of a few last-minute gifts for friends in England.

He had been sipping at his coffee, watching the passers-by on the piazza, when suddenly a strikingly lovely woman, tall with an elegant carriage and dressed in a red silk gown in the first stare of fashion, had caught his attention. With his cup still hovering near his lips, he had watched admiringly through the window as she and her even taller male companion had strolled closer.

Suddenly, the coffee in his cup had sloshed dangerously near the rim as he had recognised the woman. Good God, it was Lady Belle Smythe! Yes, Oldfield was certain of it. He had called on her when she had returned from the West Indies a few months before to offer her his condolences on her father's death. And she had always favoured vivid colours like the gown she was wearing now. So Lady Belle had fled to Paris with her mysterious lover, who must be the tall man with her.

Oldfield turned his attention to her companion, and his coffee did slosh over the rim of his cup on to the table. The Notorious Marquess! The illicit lovers stopped abruptly outside the window of the coffee house, and he was able to confirm their identities beyond a shadow of a doubt. Lady Belle's secret lover was none other than Lord Ellerton.

What a sly fox the Marquess was! He had managed to look so bored the previous night at the ambassador's dinner when Oldfield had told the scandalised guests of Lady Belle's shocking behaviour. And all the while he was her secret lover! Yes, Ellerton was a very sly fox indeed. For years he had publicly scorned ladies of quality in favour of his dramatic high fliers. But in secret...

Oldfield could tell that the lovers were arguing. Although he could not hear what was passing between them, he guessed that Lady Belle was most likely pressing the Marquess to marry her. What a bufflehead she was if she thought that she would ever get the Notorious Marquess to the altar. He would soon abandon her as he had abandoned Ivly's poor daughter, not caring a snap about the ensuing scandal.

Lord Oldfield could hardly wait to return to England and reveal to the astonished *ton* the identity of Lady Belle's lover. What a sensation it would cause! All London would be agog! And her pasty-faced little sneak of a brother would be obliged to come to Paris for a confrontation with Ellerton over the dishonour to his family. Oldfield sincerely regretted that he could not be a mouse in the corner at that meeting.

CHAPTER SIXTEEN

ON THE night after the visit to the Palais-Royal, Jason, his sister, and Annabelle were invited to dine at Tante Claudine's new apartment that the Marquess had rented for her.

The older woman confided to Annabelle how gratified and relieved she was by the progress her nephew was making in setting to rights her family's finances and reclaiming their lost property.

'*Mon Dieu*, my nephew is so good to us. Yesterday he sees the King on our behalf.'

Annabelle was startled. Jason had said nothing about his important appointment being with the King. If it had been Frederick, he would have been trumpeting it from the rooftop.

'And he rents us these better quarters,' Tante Claudine continued. 'He insists on paying for them out of his own pocket. I argue with him, but he is stone, that man.' She shrugged. 'Me, I am much relieved to have moved. No longer am I embarrassed to invite you to dine with us.' She smiled. 'How pretty you look in that gown, *chérie*. Who made it?'

Annabelle was wearing another one of Madame St Avant's creations, the blue muslin that matched her eyes. 'Madame St Avant,' she told Claudine.

'Ohhhh,' the older woman replied, her dark eyes growing round. 'There is no finer in Paris. When Jason asked me who the best is, I tell him Madame St Avant. If only I could afford a gown from her. *Chérie*, why do you look suddenly so shocked?'

Annabelle forced a smile to her lips. 'I—I did not realise how well-known she was.' Nor how expensive. Annabelle suddenly felt very gullible. The bill Jason had shown her must have been made up expressly for her benefit. But she knew, too, that she would get nowhere in attempting to find out what the true cost of the clothes had been. Jason's generosity to her only increased her burden of guilt over having tricked him into bringing her to France.

The visit to the Palais-Royal had been the last excursion that Annabelle made in public with him. Once she learned that Paris was full of English visitors who might recognise her, she refused to go anywhere with him and Rachel.

Should someone who had heard the ugly, untrue story that Frederick had spread about her see her in Jason's company, he would immediately assume that the Marquess was her secret lover. Annabelle's courage failed her at the thought of Jason's fury were he to learn that the 'poor fool' who had run off with Lady Belle was none other than himself.

Worse, she would have unwittingly brought down on his unsuspecting head the scandal that he was so eager to avoid for Rachel's sake. The world would be certain that he had brazenly passed his mistress off as his half-sister's governess, and Rachel, the third member of this irregular trio, would be tarnished, too, by association. Never mind that she was innocent. Even the slightest hint of any impropriety would be enough for her to be denied vouchers to Almacks.

Annabelle was engulfed in misery at the realisation that Rachel, whom she had come to love like a little sister, could be as much harmed by her deceit as Jason would be hurt by it.

Much as she enjoyed exploring Paris with Jason and Rachel, Annabelle could not chance being seen publicly with them.

Jason grew increasingly exasperated with her refusal to go anywhere with him. But neither his cajoling nor his anger at her queer behaviour could get her to step beyond his door in his company.

One day, a fortnight after the visit to the Palais-Royal, when she declined to accompany him and Rachel to the Palais de Justice, he reminded her irritably, 'But you expressed a strong desire to see its *grande salle*.'

Yes, Annabelle had. She still wanted to see that great arched hall and perhaps catch a peek, too, of the infamous Conciergerie prison under the building, but she dared not be seen with Jason.

'Why have you suddenly insisted upon embracing the life of a recluse?' he demanded.

Annabelle spoke vaguely of feeling a little out of curl.

'Clearly, you have been blue-devilled recently,' Jason said. 'Tell me what is troubling you.'

'Nothing is,' she insisted hastily, too hastily.

His grey eyes narrowed disbelievingly, but he did not press her. Instead, he said quietly, in a gentle voice full of concern, 'I will do whatever I can to help you if and when you wish to confide in me.'

His kind offer only made her deceit weigh more heavily upon her.

After that Jason no longer pressed her to accompany him in the afternoons because he remained at home with her, delegating to his cousins, Ambroise and Georges, the responsibility for showing Rachel about Paris. Of all the time that Annabelle had spent in Jason's company, she quickly came to cherish the most these quiet afternoons together with no one else about.

Although they enjoyed verbally jousting with each other, she realised they were of like mind on a good many things. His ironic humour delighted her, and beneath his uncivil, rakehell façade there was a depth and a breadth to him that startled Annabelle. It was clear to her now why her father had liked him so much.

She was pleasantly surprised, too, at how much respect Jason paid to her views. He was not at all like some men of her acquaintance, who assumed that all females were silly peabrains with no opinions worthy of consideration.

People mistook his abrupt manner and blunt tongue for rudeness, but it sprang from an abhorrence of dishonesty and hypocrisy and an impatience with pretence and inflated consequence rather than from a deliberate desire to wound. What

Jason hated above all else, Annabelle had discovered, was deceit.

And she had deceived him! Were she to confide the truth to him, he would despise her. And she could not bear that. She loved him too much.

One day, a month after the excursion to the Palais-Royal, an invitation to dine with the King the following night was delivered to Jason.

Rachel, seizing the gilt-edged card, asked eagerly, 'Can I go with you?'

'I fear not, puss. The invitation is only to me.'

'Oh, Jason,' Rachel cried with girlish enthusiasm, 'aren't you excited about meeting the King?'

'I already know him. He lived in Buckinghamshire in recent years, and I visited him there a number of times. I also dined with him in April when he passed through London on his way to reclaim his throne.'

Rachel, looking upon her brother with new regard, cried, 'Oh, how I should like to see the King.'

'You would be most disappointed, puss,' he assured her. 'Poor Louis is the most unkingly figure I have ever seen, even more unkingly than our own Prince Regent. Louis is grossly fat and suffers terribly from the gout.'

Rachel looked crestfallen at this description. 'Are you hoaxing me?'

'No, I speak the truth,' her brother assured her.

The following morning Jason tried to coax Annabelle into visiting the Jardin des Plantes with him and Rachel who, having been delighted by the antics of the bears in the *jardin*'s menagerie, had been begging to be taken there again. Annabelle longed to accompany them, but she could not be seen with them in such a public place.

When she could not be persuaded to change her mind, Jason and his sister went off without her.

As they stopped near the *jardin*'s entrance to watch two camels turning a wheel that pumped water up to the gardens, Rachel asked, 'When will you let me make my come-out, Jason?'

A teasing light glittered in her brother's grey eyes. 'When I can trust you not to fall in love with posturing fortune-hunters who cannot shoot straight.'

Rachel, who by now had lost her fear of her brother, giggled. 'I wish you might have seen Anna that day on the road to Newhaven. She was so brave.'

'I wish I might have, too. Is that when you fell out of love with Eustace, puss?'

'I never fell *in* love with him,' she said hotly, then added candidly, 'but I admit that I did not recognise him for a fortune-hunter either. I am wiser now, though.'

'Are you?' Jason asked in amusement.

His sister nodded gravely. 'Anna has instructed me about the kind of men who would make me unhappy, and how to recognise them.'

'Warned you against fortune-hunters and loose screws, did she?'

'Yes, and also against men with a roving eye who, although they might profess to love me, would only make me miserable with their unfaithfulness were I to marry one of them. Anna said the worst example that she could think of was Lord Garthorpe. He was, in his prime, excessively handsome and constantly unfaithful to his lovely wife, who was broken-hearted and humiliated by his affairs. Is something wrong, Jason? You look odd.'

'Nothing's wrong, puss. Only listen to Anna. She is a wise woman.'

That afternoon Jason asked Annabelle to step into his office, where he shut the door and said curtly, 'I am indebted to you for your blunt instruction to Rachel on the kind of suitors she should avoid, like men of Garthorpe's kidney.'

There was such a note of suppressed anger in Jason's voice that Annabelle thought he was displeased she had been so frank with his innocent sister.

Stung, she said defensively, 'I was not as blunt as I might have been. I did not tell her about the fine crop of bastards he planted.' Annabelle stopped short at the look on Jason's face. It was as if she had touched a raw nerve. 'Oh, dear, I am sorry that I have offended you by my frankness, but it has never bothered you before. And of all the men I met in London, I disliked Garthorpe the most. So full of his own consequence that he was certain he could melt every woman alive with his charm and good looks.'

'Did he try to melt you, Anna?'

'I am a woman, am I not?' she said evasively.

She had never seen Jason look so savage. 'Did he succeed?'

'Of course he did not,' Annabelle replied indignantly. 'He was everything I most expressly dislike: a vain, unprincipled man, brimming over with false charm and false compliments. And I told him so. You should have seen his face. I dare say no one had ever said such things to him before.' She smiled a little shyly at Jason. 'I must confess that before I met you I thought from what I had heard that you must be much like him.'

Jason looked so murderous, Annabelle hastened to say soothingly, 'Of course you do not like to be compared to him. Nor should you be. You are not at all like him.'

'Tell me about your Seasons in London, Anna,' Jason said abruptly. 'You always evade telling me anything about yourself.'

'There is nothing to tell.'

'I think there is. Why did you never marry?'

'You would be the first to tell me I am not a memorable woman.'

'To the contrary, I would brand you a liar if you tried to tell me that no man ever offered for you.'

'Not the right man,' she said evasively.

The softness vanished from his eyes, and they were again hard and searching. 'Who is the right man?'

'One that I love.'

'Have you never loved a man, Anna?' he asked gently.

The question caught her unawares, and Annabelle could feel her cheeks begin to burn.

'Ah, I see by your blush that you have,' Jason observed, his voice a little harder now. 'Who was he? Why did you not marry him?'

Annabelle cursed her colour for having betrayed her. How shocked and horrified Jason would be if she were to tell him the truth—that he was the only man she had ever loved. She hesitated.

'Why did you not marry him?' Jason repeated.

Annabelle could feel the flush on her cheeks burning brighter. 'He did not ask me,' she said in a strangled voice.

'Despite that, you are still in love with him, aren't you?'

'Yes,' she answered simply.

'Why did you come to France?'

Annabelle was caught off guard by this non sequitur. 'But you know why I came,' she stammered, 'to serve as Rachel's governess so that Claire could remain with her mother. What other reason could I have?'

'To look for someone.'

Good God, did he suspect the truth about who she really was! No, he could not, or he would be in a rage. Weakly, she said, 'You are funning me.'

'No. You seemed very eager to find the Comte de Vergennes.'

'He is an old friend, and the only person in France that I knew.' Annabelle tried to sound casual and failed. 'It is only natural that I should want to see him again, is it not?'

'Yes, but not that you should go in search of him only hours after your arrival or that you should have cried your eyes red after learning that he was dead.'

Annabelle should have known that Jason's sharp eyes would not have missed the signs of her weeping. She said weakly, 'I . . . I was very fond of him when we were children.'

Jason looked as though her answer did not satisfy him, but he said no more.

That night he dined with the King, and the next morning, when Annabelle came downstairs, he was in the hall. When she enquired how he had enjoyed his dinner at the palace, he said curtly, 'I didn't.'

She saw that his face was drawn and unhappy, and he looked as though he had not slept all night. 'Whatever is the matter, Jason?' she asked.

He did not answer her for a moment. Then he said, 'I invited a man I met at the palace last night to call on us this morning.'

At that very moment the knocker sounded. The porter opened the door to a tall, handsome man of five and thirty, fashionably dressed in a blue coat of the latest cut over a flowered brocade waistcoat with a frilled jabot at his neck.

Seeing Jason in the hallway, the visitor said, '*Excusez-moi, monseigneur.* I come very early, much earlier than you invite me.'

Annabelle stared in stunned disbelief at the figure of Jean-Louis, not dead at all but very much alive and standing before her.

'But I must know if——' her cousin was saying.

Annabelle gave a little shriek of astonished delight as it sank in upon her dazed mind that he was truly alive.

'Jean-Louis! You are not dead!' she cried, propelling herself into the arms that he opened to receive her.

'Anna, Anna!' he exclaimed in a voice full of affection as he hugged her to him. 'It is you! My dearest Anna!'

Annabelle was so overwhelmed with joy and relief at seeing her cousin that her eyes brightened with unshed tears. In her mind it was Jean-Louis, not Frederick, who was her true brother, the companion of her childhood. It was a full minute before the thunderous look on Jason's face recalled her to the danger of the present moment. She had to stop Jean-Louis from inadvertently betraying her true identity. When she had been a child she had hated his calling her Anna—the only one who had ever used that name for her. But how very, very thankful she was now.

'My dearest *friend*!' Annabelle gave Jean-Louis's hand a meaningful squeeze as she stressed the word friend. 'It has been so long since you lived with our neighbour, the Earl of Chilton. I was afraid you would have forgotten me by now.'

His dark eyes were momentarily puzzled, but he said smoothly enough, 'Ah, how could I forget my beautiful Anna?'

She had to get Jean-Louis alone so she could explain the situation to him. Turning to Jason, she said, 'Lord Ellerton, please excuse us. I wish to be private with Jean-Louis. It has been so many years since we have seen each other, and we have so much to discuss.'

'So I collect,' Jason said, so coldly she blinked.

Hastily, she led her cousin into a small reception room. Its panelled walls had been painted a restful sky blue edged in white, and the room was handsomely furnished with a gilt-framed suite of two armchairs and a settee, all upholstered in a bold floral tapestry.

As soon as the door was shut, assuring them privacy, Jean-Louis demanded, '*Mon Dieu*, when do you become the Earl of Chilton's neighbour rather than his daughter? What is this that you work as a governess? When the *monseigneur* tells me that he employs you, I do not believe it can be Annabelle. I tell him I do not think I know you. But then all night I am awake. I wonder can it be you, and I come at once this morning to see.'

'You didn't tell him that I was your cousin, did you?' she asked in alarm.

'No, because I do not think it is you. Always you hate the name Anna. Why do you use it now?'

Annabelle explained to him how her father's will had left her to Frederick's untender mercies. 'I took the position with Lord Ellerton because he was coming to France, and I was desperate to find you. There was no other way for me to get here. When I arrived, I went immediately to your *hôtel* in the Place Vendôme to find you, but that dreadful old woman there insisted that the Comte de Vergennes was dead.'

'The *hôtel* has not been in our family since the Revolution. Was the woman who told you I was dead a wizened old creature with most of her teeth missing?'

Annabelle nodded.

'That was poor Marguerite who, before the Revolution, was my father's housekeeper at the *hôtel*. Her mind dwells in the past. When she told you that the Comte was dead, she was undoubtedly speaking of my father. To her, he was the only Comte de Vergennes.'

Annabelle could not help but be angry when she thought of all the time that she had wasted when she might have been trying to contact her cousin. But what was done was done, and now she had to think of the future. 'I am desperate, Jean-Louis! You must help me!'

'I do whatever I can.'

'First, you must let me stay with you. If my identity is discovered while I am with the Marquess, there will be a terrible scandal. You must swear to me that you will not tell him under any circumstances that I am your cousin. He would be so angry I could not bear it. He has been so good to me.' She could not keep the tears from welling up.

Her cousin examined her with troubled eyes. 'I think, Anna, you love this Marquess.'

'Yes,' she admitted simply.

'Perhaps, then, it is not so very bad if there is a scandal. Perhaps then he consents to marry you.'

'No, if he would not marry Lord Ivly's daughter, he would never marry me.'

'Who is this Lord Ivly's daughter that he does not marry her?'

'It happened a score of years ago,' Annabelle began. 'She was a great beauty, and she and Ja— the Marquess were all but betrothed, but after she became pregnant with his son he refused to marry her.'

Now that Annabelle knew Jason, the story seemed incredible to her. He had such a strong sense of duty towards his family, towards his half-sister, even his aunt and her grandsons. Why had he felt no responsibility for his unborn child and no compunction about abandoning its mother?

'When the Marquess would not marry her,' Annabelle continued, 'her brother called him out. Right did not triumph. Jason shot him, although it was only a superficial wound. There was the most dreadful scandal imaginable, but Jason still refused to wed her. Two years after the baby was born, when it was clear that the Marquess would never marry her, Lord Ivly exiled both mother and son to Canada for having disgraced the family.'

Annabelle swallowed hard. She would be a great fool, indeed, to think that Jason would marry her, when he had turned his back on an Incomparable like Lord Ivly's daughter.

CHAPTER SEVENTEEN

WATCHING Anna lead the Comte into the ante-room, Jason was beset by jealousy. She had looked so radiantly happy when she had recognised de Vergennes. As Jason had watched her and the Frenchman embrace, he had felt as though his heart were splitting apart. Theirs was not the embrace of mere acquaintances or casual friends.

'My dearest Anna,' the Comte had called her. 'My dearest friend,' she had called him, and with such an odd accent on the word *friend*, as if he had been so much more. Had they been lovers all those years ago in Cambridgeshire?

Silently, Jason cursed the Comte and cursed himself for having told him about Anna. Jason had been much taken aback the previous night at the palace when he had discovered that the King's handsome and charming courtier, the one most of the women there were eagerly trying to attract, was none other than the 'late' Comte de Vergennes. The report of his death had clearly been premature.

Meeting him, Jason could easily understand how Anna, who would have been a green girl still in the schoolroom when the dashing Frenchman was at Hillbrook, would have developed a calf love for him. But Jason had assumed that the Comte would have scarcely been aware of her existence. This belief had been reinforced when Jason had mentioned his sister's governess to de Vergennes. The Comte had insisted that he remembered no Miss Anna Smith, who had been a neighbour of his uncle's at Hillbrook. Much later, however, he had come up to Jason and said that he thought perhaps he did vaguely recall an Anna Smith.

'Me, I do not think this governess can be the same woman,' he had said, 'but I beg leave to call upon you tomorrow to satisfy my curiosity.'

Jason had given him leave, but he had not expected him to call so early. Nor had Jason expected him to demonstrate more than the haziest recollection of Anna, so certain had he been that the debonair Comte would have taken no notice of a plain, provincial schoolgirl all those years before. Now, having seen the loving way that they had greeted each other, Jason knew that he had been wrong.

He had suspected that Anna had never married because she still loved the Comte. Now he was certain of it. The Comte was the man that she had admitted loving, the man who had not asked her to marry him.

And he would not ask her now. Could not, because he was already married.

Not happily. He and his wife were rarely together. She remained at his estate in Avignon while he attended the King, Jason had been told. He had watched in disgust as the Comte had moved about the room the previous night flirting outrageously with the other women guests. And now, having seen the warmth of the Comte's greeting to Anna, Jason feared that the charming Frenchman, unhappy in his marriage, might attempt to persuade Anna to become his inamorata.

Jason glared at the ante-room door. Was Anna even now in the handsome Comte's arms? When they emerged, would her lips be swollen from his passionate kisses? Jason had always thought himself immune to jealousy, but now he realised that he had never before been enough in love with a woman to be jealous of her.

But he was in love with Anna. Desperately in love with her. She continually amused and amazed him with her calm assurance and quick tongue and quiet courage. He wondered how he could ever have thought her plain. Although she was not a beauty in the classic sense—she was too tall and thin-faced for that—she could be strikingly lovely.

Was he imagining it, or had Anna bloomed like some rare flower since they had left England? She had put on much-needed weight, and her pallor had faded. Her large, brilliant eyes, the colour of the sea on a sunny summer day, sparkled with verve and humour; her engaging smile wrapped its recipients in its warmth, and her smoky, sensuous voice enveloped him like an embrace. He wanted nothing so much as to claim this lovely flower as his own.

He far preferred her to all the Incomparables he had met. None of them had possessed her spirit, humour, and clear-eyed intelligence. Nor had any of the dazzling, much-sought-after lady-birds that he had had under his protection been half so entertaining. Their expensive charms had been pale, indeed, compared to Anna's.

Anna had been good for Rachel, too. Jason was both happy and amused at the way the girl had begun to ape her. The puss could not find a better model.

His love for Anna had grown almost unnoticed during their weeks together, along with his trust in her. He liked her round dealing with him, making no pretence, as so many ladies of quality did, to a false innocence that any female no longer in the schoolroom was not likely to possess.

Anna was the one and only woman he had met since Ivly's daughter whom he had trusted. And trust, after all, was the key to love. She would, he was certain, never deceive him. And he was determined to win her. He would not give the Comte an opportunity to work his magic on Anna again and steal her away!

Jason would pack her and Rachel up and take them back to England immediately. He had accomplished what he had set out to do here in France. The finances of Tante Claudine and her grandsons were now on a firm footing. He had secretly supplemented their funds with some of his own, and he had enlisted the King's interest in the boys' futures. Yes, Jason could leave France in good conscience.

Never a man to hesitate once his mind was made up, he went upstairs to tell Rachel that they were going home.

* * *

After Annabelle emerged from the ante-room with Jean-Louis and showed him to the door, she slowly climbed the steps to her room. In the upper hallway she met Jason emerging from his sister's apartment. His glittering silver eyes studied her face, especially her mouth, with such harsh intensity she wondered uncomfortably whether there was a morsel of food on it.

'We are going home,' he told her abruptly. 'We leave for England tomorrow.'

A silent plea rose in her throat. *Oh, please, not so soon!* But she swallowed it, fighting back her tears at the realisation that he would be gone on the morrow, and she would never see him again. Nor Rachel either. And she had come to love the girl too. It was a moment before she trusted her voice enough to speak. 'I will not be going back with you.'

He looked as though she had slapped him. 'What the deuce are you talking about?'

'I am going to remain in France.'

'With Jean-Louis?' Jason snapped.

'Yes.'

'What a cosy little *ménage à trois*!'

Annabelle's eyes widened questioningly. 'What are you talking about?'

'Did your dear friend, the Comte, not tell you that he is married.'

'Married?' she echoed in surprise. Jean-Louis had not told her, but then, she had given him no chance. She had been too busy pouring out her difficulties to him.

There was a decidedly unpleasant glint in Jason's hard eyes. 'Your lover failed to reveal to you the insignificant detail that he has a wife?'

The impact of his words stuck Annabelle with the force of a physical blow, and she put out her hand to steady herself on the railing of the balustrade. 'Jean-Louis is *not* my lover!'

'*Is* not?' Jason demanded furiously. 'Would I have been more accurate to say your once and future lover!'

'No, you would not have!' she cried, her own temper rising.

'I fear that I have sorely underestimated the magnitude of French hospitality, then.' Jason's voice dripped with sarcasm. 'Why would a man, any man, but most particularly one of the Comte de Vergennes's charm, immediately upon meeting a casual acquaintance that he had not set eyes on in years offer her a home?'

His eyes bored into Annabelle like steel daggers. She dared not tell him the truth. If she admitted that Jean-Louis was her cousin, she would also be admitting to Jason that she was Lady Belle, the current scandal of England, and admitting, too, how outrageously she had deceived him. She could not bring herself to do that when he was already so angry.

'Do you think the Comte's offer springs from the goodness of his heart?' Jason demanded scornfully. 'I had not thought you so naïve.'

'You do Jean-Louis a grave injustice.' Her voice cracked with emotion, and she rushed past Jason into her room, throwing the door shut after her.

But instead of slamming closed, it bounced back against its hinges as Jason stalked through it. This time it was he who sent it crashing shut behind him.

She whirled to face him. 'How dare you come in here?'

But he ignored her protest. He grabbed her arms, towering above her, his face a study in fury, his long, lean fingers biting painfully into her flesh. 'It is you who does the Comte too much justice! You came to France under my protection and, by God, you will return to England under it! It is my duty to protect you from this folly.'

'It . . . is not folly,' she protested weakly.

'Do you love him so much that you have lost all sense of propriety?'

Tears glistened in her eyes. 'I do not love Jean-Louis! Nor do I stay here because I love him, but only because there is nothing in England for me to return to.'

Her words seemed to extinguish his rage like water on fire, and he said softly, 'But there is a reason for you to return. Rachel and I need you in England.'

She shook her head mournfully. 'No, Claire is Rachel's governess.' Jason had relaxed his painful grip on her arms, but he had not removed his hands, and he was standing so close to her she could hardly catch her breath. 'Claire is my friend, Jason, and I cannot usurp her position.'

'No, nor do I wish you to. I intend for Mrs Potter to continue as Rachel's governess.'

His answer confused Annabelle. 'So, you see, there is nothing for me to return to. I have no home in England.'

'You have one with me if you wish it,' he said gently.

She gasped, her eyes widening in shock and pain. There could only be one possible interpretation of his words. He was offering her a carte blanche!

'Are you so very much shocked?' he asked with such tenderness in his voice that for one mad moment she yearned to throw herself into his arms and accept his offer no matter how disreputable it was. But then sanity returned to her. He would use her as he had his other convenients. That was his style. He would soon forget her, but she would love him forever. Her voice trembled with emotion. 'I cannot accept your carte blanche.'

His hands dropped away from her arms, and he looked as though she had slapped him. 'Nor am I offering you one, you little fool,' he said savagely. 'I am asking you to marry me.'

For a moment she could only stare at him, unable to conceal the violent emotions that tore at her. She was wildly in love with him. Never had she wanted anything so much as to accept his offer, but in light of his disreputable past she could not believe that he could be serious about making her his wife. 'Are . . . are you hoaxing me?' she enquired weakly.

'I am not in the habit of asking a woman to marry me in jest,' he said, affronted. 'Nor, for that matter, of asking at all. You are the first.'

'But you cannot want to marry me, a mere governess,' Annabelle stammered.

'I told you once that I was quite democratic,' he teased, his arms stealing around her.

But she was not convinced. She remembered how he had rejected that incomparable beauty, Lord Ivly's daughter, even though she had been carrying his son. Annabelle's distress was mirrored in her face. 'Why would you want to marry me when you would ... would not ...' She faltered at the sudden fury on Jason's face. His arms dropped away from her, and he stepped back.

There was a long, angry pause, and then he finished for her. 'When I would not marry Lord Ivly's daughter?'

Annabelle nodded unhappily.

'You find my behaviour unforgivable?' he asked in an odd, strangled voice.

She raised her troubled gaze to met his squarely. 'No, inexplicable. It seems so unlike you to act as you did.'

'Thank you for the benefit of the doubt,' he said sardonically. 'You are the only person whose opinion I ever cared enough about to tell the truth to, but you must not repeat it. It would serve no purpose to dredge up that old scandal again.'

'Does no one know the truth?'

'Five of us did. She, I, her father and mine, and——' Jason hesitated.

Annabelle, remembering the duel between him and Charles Ivly, prompted, 'And her brother.'

'No, not Charles,' Jason said bitterly. 'Neither she nor her father ever told the poor boy the truth. Instead, that evil man urged his son, who was no match for me with either pistols or swords, to challenge me to a duel in defence of his sister's honour. Her honour! What a joke! She had none.' It was as if all the bitterness in the world had been distilled into his voice. 'At least I do not have Charles's death on my conscience. The wound I was forced to give him was minor, and he recovered quickly enough. I hated to have to hurt him, but if I had not, he would have happily killed me. And I cannot say that I would have blamed him, thinking what he did.'

'But who was the other person who knows the truth, if it is not her brother?'

'Lord Garthorpe.'

'Lord Garthorpe,' she echoed, thinking of that blond-haired, blue-eyed Adonis with his dimpled chin, his heart-shaped birthmark beside his mouth, and his crop of bastards. A terrible suspicion flashed through her mind. 'Good God, was he...?'

Jason nodded bleakly. 'Yes, he was the father of the child whose paternity she so generously tried to foist on me. He was, of course, already married, so old Ivly hit upon having her spring parson's mousetrap on me. She went along with the idea. She would have been far wiser to have picked one of her other admirers, but I offered her the highest rank and greatest fortune.'

Annabelle flinched at the sarcastic loathing in Jason's voice.

'I won't scruple to tell you that I was bewitched when first she set her cap for me. She was an Incomparable with a face like an angel. When she professed herself madly in love with me, I was too young and foolish to suspect that this might be less than the truth, and I thought myself the luckiest man in the world. It was midsummer moon with me. I would have allowed myself to be led posthaste to the altar had not I chanced one night to see her sneak off with Garthorpe. I followed them and was soon brutally disabused of my romantic notions.'

Although he spoke with a cynical sarcasm, she could see reflected in his eyes even all these years later some of the anguished betrayal and humiliation he had felt that night, and her hand unconsciously reached out to touch his arm comfortingly.

'I refused to have anything more to do with her, but by then her pregnancy was beginning to show. Old Ivly arranged to have us found in a compromising situation during a large house party at Castle Howard. I awoke out of a sound sleep in the middle of the night to a room full of shocked faces and her in bed beside me. When I still refused to marry her, she swore that I was the father of her unborn child. I knew there was no way that could be true. But, after that staged scene at Castle Howard, no one was likely to believe otherwise.'

No wonder Jason did not trust women, Annabelle thought.

His face was drawn into tortured lines. 'I would not, I could not, accept another man's bastard as the future Marquess of Ellerton. For four hundred years the title had passed in an unbroken line from father to son, and I owed it both to my ancestors and to my descendants to preserve the lineage. That was why I refused to marry her.'

Until now Annabelle had wondered how his strong sense of familial duty and loyalty had permitted him to abandon Ivly's daughter, but now she understood that had been the very thing that had required him to do so. She asked him sadly, 'Why did you never defend yourself publicly.'

He shrugged. 'It would have done no good. There was no way to prove the truth, and after the scene at Castle Howard it is doubtful that anyone would have believed me. Meanwhile, old Ivly was certain that he could coerce me into marrying his daughter if only he made a big enough scandal, but he was wrong.'

'Was that why he waited until two years after the boy was born to exile him and his mother to Canada—he thought you would eventually capitulate and marry her?'

'No, he'd known it was hopeless long before that. The child, however, had the misfortune to be born the image of his father, even to the dimple in his chin and that little birthmark beside his mouth. It would have been hard to keep up the fiction that a blond, blue-eyed boy who looked exactly like Garthorpe was my son.'

'What a dreadful time it must have been for you.'

'The worst was my father. He was furious at me for having brought shame upon the family name and contemptuous of my stupidity for allowing myself to become ensnared in such a mess.'

'But you were only a calfling.'

'Yes, and a very unhappy one. For a time I was even hell-bent on bringing my existence to a quick end. In the process I acquired quite a reputation on the field of honour.' His lips quirked sardonically. 'Not that there's much honour in it that I can see!'

Annabelle's hands were intertwined with Jason's now, squeezing them comfortingly.

'Since I had already acquired a scandalous reputation, I decided to live up to it, but I never again wanted anything to do with so-called ladies. That left the demi-monde.' The harshness suddenly evaporated from his eyes as he regarded Annabelle lovingly. 'You, my darling, are the only woman I have met since Ivly's daughter whom I knew that I could trust never to deceive me.'

But she had deceived him! Annabelle felt as though her heart were crumpling in upon itself. She had hidden her real identity from him and might yet bring down upon his undeserving head another dreadful scandal. When he learned the truth, his trust in her would be shattered beyond repair.

Suddenly he took her in his arms and kissed her, a long, loving, passionate kiss that left her trembling with desire and fear. 'Now, my darling, will you be my wife?' he asked caressingly.

For a moment, torn between longing and sorrow, she could not speak. Her mind was a boiling cauldron of bitter thoughts. She could not accept his offer until she told him the truth, but if she did so, he might no longer want her. She knew how much he despised deceit and dishonesty. Would his love for her turn to hate for having deceived him?

What was she to do? She could not just blurt out the truth to him now. Not when he was looking at her with eyes that spoke silent volumes of love. She could not bring herself to destroy that love, and in the process her own heart. Her head was pounding so that she could no longer think straight.

'I had not thought my offer would so distress you,' Jason said stiffly. 'It is the Comte you love, isn't it?'

'No, it is you whom I love,' she cried frantically, unable to bear the wounded look in those beautiful silver eyes. 'If you believe nothing else, Jason, believe that I love you.'

Her words brought such a glow of happiness to his hard face that she knew she would treasure the memory of it all the rest of her life.

He took her into his arms, and his mouth descended towards hers. It stopped a scant inch away, so close to hers that she could feel his warm caressing breath upon it, and he said, 'Then, my darling, we will be married as quickly as I can arrange it.'

She tried to edge away, 'But, Jason——'

'What is it?' he asked, his face clouding with concern. 'Are you repelled by my misspent past? I cannot justify it, but I will point out that the only difference between me and most of my peers is that I never hid my convenients from public view. If they were worthy of gracing my bed, they were worthy of gracing my arm in public.'

And Annabelle liked him the better for that. 'I am not repelled by your past, only a trifle concerned about your future constancy.'

'You need not be, my darling. I would not marry you if I did not intend to be as faithful to you as I know that you will be to me.' He smiled at her with such aching tenderness that she could no longer resist the tantalising closeness of his lips, and she let them claim hers.

Once they did, she was lost. She loved him beyond reason, and her courage temporarily failed her. Jason was so happy, and so was she. She could not spoil it quite yet by confessing that she had deceived him. Surely this afternoon would be soon enough to tell him? Maybe by then, she rationalised desperately, he would not be angry.

CHAPTER EIGHTEEN

ANNABELLE'S brother sat in a closed carriage parked across the street from the Paris *hôtel* that Lord Ellerton had hired, trying to screw up his courage to confront his lordship. What if Oldfield had been wrong, and the woman with Ellerton was not Frederick's sister?

No one in England had been more dumbfounded than young Chilton when Lord Oldfield had returned from Paris with the news that Annabelle's secret lover was none other than the Notorious Marquess. Although Frederick had spread far and wide the story that his sister had eloped, he had not for an instant thought that there was a particle of truth in his tale. Its purpose had been to ruin her.

Frederick had been confounded to learn that Annabelle had obliged him in this endeavour by actually running away with a man. And not just any man, but the Notorious Marquess, guaranteeing that Annabelle's reputation would be blackened beyond redemption. Thanks to Lord Oldfield, all London was abuzz with their shocking flight. It was the chief topic of conversation at every squeeze. No man would marry Annabelle now, least of all, Frederick thought with a smirk, her lover, whose antipathy for marriage was well known.

Back in England, Chilton had relished playing the role of shocked and outraged brother to the hilt, loudly announcing that he would go to France to confront the illicit lovers.

Now that he was there, however, he eyed Ellerton's door with more than a little dread. If only he could be certain that Annabelle was living under the Marquess's protection. They were such an unlikely couple. Ellerton was famous for squiring only the most gorgeous demi-reps. Frederick could not conceive how he could possibly have been persuaded to take up with a plain, proper creature like Annabelle. Or she with him.

Her brother was still staring undecidedly at the Marquess's door when it opened. A tall, striking woman, very fashionably dressed in a yellow gown and a dashing wide-brimmed hat decorated with yellow silk roses and ribands came out. It was clear from her exchange with the porter that she lived there. As she started briskly down the street, Frederick belatedly recognised his sister. He clasped his hands together in delight. So Oldfield had been right!

A less greedy man than Frederick would have rejoiced at his success in ruining his sister's reputation and let it go at that. But he could not bear to let pass any opportunity that offered the smallest promise of even a paltry profit. When he had heard Oldfield's story, Frederick had hit upon how he could reap an additional financial benefit for himself. Ellerton was famous for squandering his blunt on his birds of paradise and making them handsome settlements when he was done with them.

When Frederick collected his sister, he would first demand that Ellerton, who held matrimony repugnant, must wed her. Her brother considered this demand a stroke of genius, for it would serve the double purpose of raising the Marquess's hackles, thereby assuring that he would never marry Annabelle, and of making him more amenable to a handsome settlement when the demand was withdrawn.

Frederick had been so proud of his scheme he had bragged of it to Mr Quigg. Although the solicitor rarely displayed any restraint when it came to greed, this time he had strongly advised Frederick to forget it, saying bluntly, 'You'd be a bloody fool to try that with Ellerton. He's not a cove to be threatened.'

But Frederick was never a man to heed another's advice if there was blunt to be gained. The thought of the amount which might be extracted from Ellerton was too tempting for Frederick to pass up. Furthermore, he remembered with vivid humiliation that night the Marquess had exposed his cheating to the assembled players at White's. How wonderful it would be to see Ellerton squirm as he had made Frederick squirm.

When Chilton had still been in England, he had thought with enormous relish of approaching his nemesis with right on his side, playing the outraged head of the family, demanding that Ellerton marry his sister. Now that the moment was at hand, however, Frederick's palms were sweating and his stomach was churning at the prospect of facing the Marquess. If only he were not such a large and forbidding man. Aware of how unnerving he found Ellerton face-to-face, Frederick had taken the precaution of writing out and memorising an Outraged Brother speech, but now he quailed at delivering it.

Fear battled with greed in his soul, and it was a near thing. But greed, as it always did in Frederick's case, triumphed. He descended from his coach and crossed the street to the Marquess's hotel.

When Jason was told that Lord Chilton was awaiting him in the drawing room, he could not believe it until he had confirmed his caller's identity with his own eyes.

'So it is you, Chilton,' he said coldly. 'I own I am astonished that you would come here.'

'Under the circumstances, I would think you would be more astonished if I did not.' The Earl launched into what sounded to Jason suspiciously like a memorised speech. 'It is my duty as head of my family to protect my sister, and I am here to insist that you marry her!'

For a bewildered moment Jason wondered if Chilton had run mad. Then, in a voice so cold that it could have frozen boiling water, he demanded, 'Why should I marry a woman I have never met?'

His visitor looked genuinely astonished. 'That won't fadge,' he cried. 'All England knows that you have brought her to Paris with you.'

'What the deuce are you talking about?' Jason thundered so violently that Frederick winced. 'I heard that your sister had run off with her lover, but I have no notion of their whereabouts.'

'You cannot flummery me!' Chilton cried indignantly. 'I saw Annabelle leaving here only a few minutes ago. Dressed in the first stare of fashion, too, in a new yellow gown and an expensive hat.' Frederick smirked. 'Do not try to deny that it was Annabelle. I know my own sister!'

'Anna*belle*!' Jason exclaimed, feeling like a man who had just been struck by lightning. Good God, could Lady Annabelle Smythe be his Anna Smith? The last names, although spelled differently, were pronounced the same. He silently answered his own question. Yes, she could! It explained so many contradictions about her that had puzzled him.

The truth left him speechless. He was overcome by a seething mixture of emotions: murderous anger at both her and her slimy little brother for having set him up like a plump pigeon for the plucking, and contempt for himself at having been so easily gulled. But above all, he was torn by the most bitter hurt and disillusionment that he had ever known in his life. The one, the only woman that he had loved enough to want to make his wife was even more perfidious than Ivly's wretched daughter! The pain of this realisation was almost more than Jason could bear.

His eyes narrowed into furious slits. 'So you foisted her off on me by disguising her as a governess?'

'I do not know what kind of story you might have concocted to try to hide your illicit relationship with my sister,' Frederick said unpleasantly, 'but I can promise you that no one will believe it.'

'I dare say you are right,' Jason said bitterly. He remembered that long-ago night at Castle Howard, and once again he was beset by the same sense of being trapped in a nightmare from which there was no awakening.

As the shock of Chilton's revelations wore off, it was replaced by a rage so intense that Jason could scarcely keep from throttling the disgusting little dandy. And that was nothing compared to what he would like to do to Chilton's sister. He had been so thoroughly duped he had even thrown her the handkerchief. But he would never marry the lying, heartless jade now.

Frederick, apparently encouraged by the Marquess's admission, drew himself up to his full height which, compared to Ellerton, was not very tall. Assuming an outraged stance and tone, he resumed his declamation. 'I insist that you marry my sister. My family's honour——'

'What a fool you are, Chilton!' Jason interrupted. 'You should have consulted your sister before approaching me with your demand. By failing to do so, you have achieved the exact opposite of your goal. I will never marry her now.'

'Now?' Chilton gasped, so shocked that he momentarily forgot his speech.

'Where are you staying in Paris?' Jason demanded impatiently. When Frederick told him, the

Marquess said, 'Your sister will be delivered to you there within the hour. Now, get out of here!'

'I cannot permit you to ruin my sister!' Chilton cried, at last remembering his lines. 'Such an ugly slur on my family's honour! It is my duty to protect both it and my sister.'

'I sincerely hope that means you intend to call me out. You will not be the first brother to have done so under such circumstances.'

From the look on Chilton's face it was clear that not only had he no such intention, but the thought terrified him.

'But be warned,' Jason continued ominously, 'that I liked poor Charlie Ivly. That is why he is still alive. I despise you.'

Annabelle's brother could manage only a frightened, inarticulate squeak.

'Get out of here, you little snake,' Jason snapped, 'before *I* call *you* out for attempting to perpetrate this fraud upon me!'

Chilton fled from the room in undignified haste.

Annabelle had paid no attention to the closed carriage parked across the street when she had set out on a brisk walk in the hope of shoring up her flagging courage and restoring her disordered senses to some semblance of coherent thought. How could one person be simultaneously so wildly happy and terribly miserable? In retrospect, she knew that she should have told Jason the truth the instant he had made her his offer. She hated herself for not having done so. The longer she postponed telling him, the worse she was making the situation. She must stop her procrastination and do so immediately. Resolutely, she turned around and went back to the *hôtel*.

When she reached it, she was surprised to learn that Jason was closeted in the drawing room with a caller—an English m'lord.

Annabelle wondered who it could be. She dared not be seen in Jason's house by any Englishman. She retired to the small ante-room, leaving word that she wished to talk to the Marquess as soon as he was free.

Standing before a big gilt-framed mirror, she removed her wide-brimmed hat trimmed with the yellow roses and ribands. She was placing the chapeau on a small marble-topped table under the mirror, when the door flew open, and Jason, in as raging a fury as she had ever seen any man, stalked in.

'You lying witch, Lady Annabelle Smythe!' he snapped.

She flinched. 'How did you . . .'

'So you don't bother to deny your true identity now that you have made us the scandal of England.'

'Not *you*, Jason. No one knows that I am with you.'

'Your brother assures me that all England knows that you have eloped to Paris with me!'

Annabelle was suddenly assailed by such dizziness that she had to put her hands on the tapestry-upholstered back of one of the armchairs to steady herself. 'Frederick is here!' she gasped in dismay, wondering how he could possibly have found her.

'He is here,' Jason replied grimly, 'and you will catch cold trying to play the innocent with me! You and your snake of a brother will not succeed in your little plot to get me to the altar. I will never marry you now.'

That Jason would be furious with her—and justly so—for having deceived him about her true identity, Annabelle had known, but that he would so readily believe that she was in league with her awful brother in a plot to force him to marry her shocked and wounded her.

'You know me better than to think that I would consort with that odious little toad in a nefarious scheme like that!' she cried.

He gave her a look of such scorn and contempt it shrivelled her soul.

'It turns out I did not know you at all, did I, Lady Belle?' He spat out her name as though it were a bad taste in his mouth. 'What other reason could you have had for foisting yourself upon me, disguised as a governess, you lying vixen?'

Annabelle was ashen-faced. How could Jason convict her like this without even hearing her side of the story? 'I was not in league with my brother!' she cried. 'I was trying to escape him.'

Desperately she explained to Jason why she had deceived him so that he would bring her to France. But she could tell by the rigid, furious set of his face that he did not believe her. That he would never believe her again.

'Liar!' he snapped when she finished. 'When were you at last going to tell me your true identity, Lady Belle? When it was too late for me to renege? Perhaps after we had exchanged our wedding vows, when we had to sign the marriage register? Or did you think that I would be too besotted to notice the slight change in your name when you signed it, you wretched, heartless jade!'

'You are being a fool!' she protested.

'No, Lady Belle, I am through being the fool! You will never hoax me again!'

'But you've got to believe me!' she cried in frustration.

'Your story is absurd on the face of it!'

'Absurd?' she echoed in disbelief. 'Why?'

'Because your brother is trying to force me to marry you, and if the tale you tell were true, the last thing that he would want is for me to marry you.'

Annabelle looked at him in astonishment. 'I don't understand.'

'Then do let me explain it to you,' Jason said scathingly. 'If we were to marry, as your brother insists that we do, he would immediately lose control of your inheritance.'

'No, Mr Quigg said that the trust Papa drew up gives Frederick control of it for my lifetime.'

'Then Mr Quigg cannot be much of a lawyer. Even if your father executed such a document, it would never withstand your husband's legal challenge. Your property would legally belong to him. I could break the trust in a trice if I married you.

But I assure you that not even such a great fortune as yours would tempt me to the altar with you now. Nor will it tempt any other man worth marrying!'

Annabelle's legs would no longer support her. She sank into one of the tapestry chairs and buried her head in her hands, her thoughts a whirl of sickening confusion.

'God, but I would like to murder you, Lady Belle! Once again I learn that I am the centre of a scandal that was not of my making. If it were only my reputation, I would not care a ninepin, but what about Rachel? How could you do this to her? But you were so desperate for a husband of rank that you would not scruple to hurt an innocent girl.'

Annabelle, who loved Rachel as if she were her own sister, was horrified and grievously hurt that Jason could think her guilty of such dreadful motives. Somehow she had to make him understand. 'Why would I be so eager to marry you for title and rank when I am a lady and an heiress in my own right?' she demanded.

He looked at her with such hating eyes that her heart seemed to shatter into tiny pieces. 'No doubt because you are a pattern copy of your greedy, grasping sneak of a brother who, no matter how much money he has, will never have enough!'

His cruel words ignited Annabelle's own temper. How could this man who had professed to love her hurl such dreadful accusations at her head, refusing to give any credence to her explanation, refusing to give her the slightest benefit of the doubt? Surely all the weeks that they had spent together should have given him a better understanding of her character.

'When I think how close I came to shackling myself to you,' Jason said in a voice of loathing, 'I am filled with almost as much contempt for myself as for you. You are worse than Ivly's daughter ever was. At least she had an unborn child to protect, but you, *you*...' Jason was so choked by rage that he could not continue.

It occurred to Annabelle that she was confronting a man in such a fury that he was beyond rational thought, but that was no comfort to her.

When he was able to speak again, it was to tell her, 'You have thirty minutes to pack your belongings. My coach will be waiting to deliver you to your brother.'

Annabelle cried in disbelief, 'You would not, you could not be so cruel as to send me back to Frederick!'

'What is this!' Jason demanded sarcastically. 'Are we re-enacting *The Prisoner of Iago* again? Are you trying to play Desdemona to your brother's Iago? I regret to have to spoil your little farce, but I decline to play Prince William!'

With that Jason turned and slammed out of the door.

Annabelle, feeling as though Wellington's army had marched across her heart, trampling it into dust, forced herself to go up to her room where she hurriedly changed from the yellow gown that Jason had given her into one of Tante Marie's old black dresses. She stuffed only the few articles that she had brought to France into her battered leather portmanteau, leaving behind the wardrobe that Jason had bought for her.

Then, with tears she was powerless to prevent coursing down her cheeks, she sneaked out of the servants' entrance, past a startled maid, and set off for Jean-Louis's. She dared not take the time to say good-bye to Rachel. Annabelle had to get away before Jason insisted on delivering her back to Frederick.

CHAPTER NINETEEN

LORD ELLERTON had promised that Annabelle would be returned to her brother within the hour. When she had not come by that night, Frederick grew increasingly uneasy. His sister had such a quick and convincing tongue. Had she somehow managed to talk Ellerton out of bringing her back? Chilton vacillated between his fear of facing the angry Marquess again and his terror that somehow Annabelle's fortune might slip from his hands. It would be impossible for him to make do on his own paltry inheritance.

Finally, he hit upon the idea of calling upon Ellerton at ten, when the Marquess was certain to be out enjoying the licentious delights that Paris offered in abundance. Frederick would collect his sister and leave behind a note that he would drop his demand that Ellerton marry Annabelle in exchange for a trifling financial settlement.

Carefully, Chilton wrote out the note and headed for Ellerton's *hôtel*.

But to Frederick's dismay, the Marquess was at home, and there was nothing to do but pocket the note he had planned to leave and allow himself to be led on unsteady legs into the drawing room while praying fervently that Ellerton's temper had cooled since that morning.

The Marquess was sprawled carelessly upon a sofa that looked too delicate to bear his large frame. To Frederick's enormous relief, an expression of cold indifference had replaced the burning rage that had gripped Ellerton earlier in the day. He did not rise to greet his visitor, nor did he invite him to be seated, and Frederick was forced to remain standing before him.

Ellerton quirked a questioning eyebrow at his visitor, enquiring in hopeful accents, 'Have you come to call me out?'

This unpromising opening unnerved Frederick, and his answer was not quite as steady as he would have liked. 'I have come to collect my sister.'

'But she is with you,' the Marquess said in a bored tone. 'She left here not fifteen minutes after you did.'

'Don't try to gammon me,' Frederick cried.

'It is not I who go about gammoning people, prigging bracelets, or cheating at cards.' Ellerton's grey eyes were as icy as his tone.

Frederick was much alarmed at the possibility that Annabelle might have disappeared again. 'Where the blazes could she have gone?'

His exclamation brought a flicker of interest to Ellerton's hard eyes, but he said coldly, 'To perdition, I hope.'

'You must have some idea where she is,' Frederick pressed.

'Not I,' the Marquess said with a negligent shrug. 'She is your sister. I advise you to keep better track of her. It will be very difficult for you to insist that

I marry her when you do not even know where she is.'

Frederick eagerly seized upon this opening. 'It is no longer my wish that you marry her.'

Ellerton no longer looked bored. 'Why is that?'

'I have concluded that it would be wrong for me to let my sister, despite her scandalous conduct, marry a man of your character.'

A strange little smile curled Ellerton's mouth. 'Is that so?'

Frederick, taking the odd smile as an encouraging sign, hurried on. 'Yes, it is so. I do, however, insist upon financial redress from you for having ruined her in the eyes of the world and for humiliating my family's proud name in the process. Provided we can agree on a sum, I will withdraw my insistence that you marry her.'

'What sum did you have in mind, Chilton?' Ellerton asked, looking so relieved that Frederick hastily revised upward by an extortionate amount the figure he had planned to demand.

'Twenty thousand pounds.'

The Marquess looked shocked. 'Far too steep,' he complained. 'I would rather marry your sister than pay that price.'

Frederick was so certain that with a little pressure Ellerton would capitulate that he was prepared to drive a hard bargain. 'Then it shall be the altar for you,' he said with the complacent smirk of one who knows he holds the upper hand.

'I see it shall be,' Jason said with a regretful sigh. 'By the way, how did you know that your sister was in Paris?'

Frederick blinked at this unexpected question. 'Lord Oldfield saw her with you, publicly flaunting herself on your arm like one of your common demi-reps.'

'My demi-reps are never in the common way, Chilton,' Jason said in a dangerously soft voice that disconcerted his listener, 'but it is your sister that we are discussing. If I do agree to marry her, can you guarantee her presence at the wedding? Only think how embarrassing it will be for you if I stand ready at the altar to make an honest woman of her and she proves to be a jilt.'

Frederick stared at him in disbelief. 'You cannot want to marry her!'

'No,' the Marquess said, his hard face drawn into inscrutable lines, 'but I hold twenty thousand pounds too dear a price to pay to escape parson's mousetrap.'

'Ten thousand, then,' Frederick bargained, beginning to wish that he had heeded Mr Quigg's advice instead of his own greed.

'Still too high,' the Marquess said with a yawn. 'Shall we set the wedding date now?'

'Yes, we shall,' Frederick agreed, calling his lordship's bluff.

'I'll arrange with the British ambassador to marry us at the embassy. Will tomorrow be soon enough?'

'Tomorrow?' Frederick squeaked.

'Yes, tomorrow,' Jason said urbanely. 'I trust you will be able to produce your sister by then.'

'Five thousand pounds,' Frederick cried desperately.

'No,' the Marquess said with a negligent shrug. 'It is time I took a wife, and, in light of your demands, it might as well be your sister. Now, if you were to withdraw your demand for a payment...'

Frederick hastily did so.

The Marquess smiled lazily, a strange gleam in his grey eyes.

Frederick choked with rage as he realised that once again he had been bested by the Marquess. 'Damn you, Ellerton!' he cried, turning to depart.

'Where are you going, Chilton?'

'I am leaving,' Frederick ground out. 'We have nothing further to discuss.'

He was stopped in his tracks by the Marquess's voice, low and strangely chilling. 'But we have a good deal yet to discuss, Chilton. You see, I have decided that, even though you have withdrawn your demand, I wish to marry your sister after all.'

Frederick, unable to believe his ears, whirled around. Ellerton was still lounging negligently on the sofa.

'But y-y-you can't want to marry her!' Frederick stammered. 'Why would you?'

Ellerton's grey eyes were as cold and hard as granite. 'To disoblige the pair of you, of course.'

Frederick could readily believe that, but he could not let the marriage happen. 'You will regret it,' he cried. 'You will live under the cat's paw. She is not at all the kind of woman you favour.'

'How complimentary you are of your sister,' Jason observed.

'It is true,' Frederick cried defensively. 'She is a termagant who will make your life miserable. You are mad to marry her!'

Ellerton rose lazily from the sofa. 'But you have failed to point out your sister's one great attraction: the vast fortune she inherited from your father.'

Annabelle's brother stared aghast at the older, larger man who towered more than a head above him. 'But you are swimming in lard!' he protested. 'Why would you want her inheritance too?'

The Notorious Marquess shrugged carelessly. 'You have no conception of how expensive my uncommon demi-reps are. And there are some renovations I wish to make to Elmdale. It was built in Elizabethan times, and it lacks certain modern comforts. I have a yearning to enlarge and redo it in the Georgian manner.' His grey eyes narrowed suddenly. 'For your sake, Chilton, I hope that you have been a good trustee of your sister's fortune. Rest assured that I shall demand a full accounting of every groat.'

The Marquess was regarding Frederick with that same knowing, contemptuous look that had been on his face that night at White's, when he had caught him cheating at cards.

'I shall naturally go over each and every expenditure that you have made on her behalf,'

Ellerton continued smoothly, his look growing more merciless. 'Should I find any discrepancies, I will pursue them ruthlessly. I will not have my wife cheated.'

His cold, precise words were not so much a warning as a vow. Although Frederick's understanding was not superior, he would have had to be a cod's head not to know that Ellerton had somehow divined that he had been embezzling his sister's inheritance and that the Marquess would not rest until the money had been restored.

CHAPTER TWENTY

ANNABELLE arrived at Jean-Louis's nurturing a tiny hope, as stubborn as it was foolish, that Jason would come to his senses and realise she was not the awful creature he had branded her.

Jason's indictment had opened her eyes to Fredrick's motive for isolating her at Moorlands and spreading the scurrilous story that she had run off with a lover. He had wanted to assure she never married so her inheritance would remain firmly in his control. *Never underestimate what a man will do when great money or power is at stake,* Jason had said, and he had been right.

But Annabelle was as baffled as Jason at why her brother should now be insisting that the Marquess marry her. It made no sense, and more than anything, this demand of Frederick's was what had condemned her in Jason's mind.

Nevertheless, she was certain that once his rage cooled he would comprehend the error of his thinking and would come after her, begging her forgiveness for having so cruelly misjudged her. Annabelle drew great solace for her lacerated sensibilities by playing out in her mind several different versions of this affecting scene. All of them had in common a contrite Jason pledging his undying love for her and assuring her that he could not live without her, as she could not live without him.

But when hours lengthened into days with no sign of Jason, contrite or otherwise, her hope flickered out like a candle-flame in the breeze. In its place, the wound inflicted by his slanderous estimation of her festered, and Annabelle grew increasingly angry with him.

By the morning of her third day at Jean-Louis's, a heartbroken Annabelle was convinced that she would never see Jason again. Nor could he have truly loved her. If he had, he would have known that she would not have conspired with her dreadful brother. Trust was the cornerstone of love, and Jason had not trusted her enough to believe the truth. The more Annabelle dwelled upon his rank injustice to her in this regard, the more hurt and outraged she became.

After a breakfast that she hardly touched, she went dejectedly towards the stairs to go up to her room. Jean-Louis said sympathetically, 'Perhaps the *monseigneur* does not know where you are.'

'He knows that I am with you,' Annabelle cried. 'There is no other place I could have gone. And I do not want to see him! I am so furious with him that he could think...' Her sentence trailed off as she turned and marched up the stairs, her back as straight and stiff as a poker. She was almost to the top of the staircase, when there was a violent pounding on Jean-Louis's door.

Turning to see who was there, Annabelle's knees grew so weak at the sight of Jason's tall, muscular figure filling the doorway she had to grasp the handrail of the worked-iron balustrade for support. This movement attracted his attention. Seeing her standing on the stairs, he said harshly, 'I knew I would find you here, you maddening piece of baggage.'

He did not look in the least contrite, and he sounded as angry as he had been the last time Annabelle had seen him. So much for contrition and undying love, she thought bitterly. Her heart, which had leapt for joy at the sight of him, tripped and crashed over her indignation and pain at his insulting misreading of her character. Clearly, he had come to hurl more insults at her head, and she had no intention of listening to him. In icy tones she told Jean-Louis to inform the Marquess that she was not at home to him.

Jason glared up at her. 'Why not?'

Jean-Louis, looking unhappily from one to the other, replied placatingly, 'My cousin, she is angry with you.'

'*She* is angry with *me*!' Jason exploded. 'Who the hell got us into this wretched coil?'

He brushed past her cousin and started up the steps two at a time towards her, his face as black as a storm cloud. Annabelle's courage deserted her. She did not think she would be able to maintain her composure if Jason delivered another stinging tirade, and she would not embarrass herself by crying in front of him.

Turning, she fled into her room, but by the time she got through its door, Jason was hard on her heels.

As he sent the door crashing shut after them, she turned to face him defiantly. 'Get out of here! I have nothing to say to you.'

'Good,' he snapped. 'That means you won't interrupt what I have to say to you!'

Jason advanced toward her with a grace and purpose that made her think of a black panther trapping his prey. He looked exhausted. His dark, lean face was set in grim, uncompromising lines. The probing silver eyes were narrowed, and his sardonic mouth had tightened into a thin horizontal slash. He looked so furious and forbidding that Annabelle inwardly quailed, but she managed to say with credible bravura, 'Nor will I listen to you! You have already said far too much to me!'

'You are wrong! I have a good deal more to tell you, Lady Belle,' he said with a contemptuous inflection on the name.

'Don't call me that!' she cried. 'My name is Annabelle.'

'There are a good many less pretty names that I would like to call you,' he ground out. 'Damn you, you little vixen, why didn't you tell me the truth about yourself? I become so incensed every time I think about it, I could break that lovely neck of yours. And now, after all the trouble you have caused me, you have the effrontery to try to refuse to see me!'

'You were in no great hurry to see me. It has been three days!'

He said through clenched jaw, 'I have been exceedingly busy with the odious and difficult task of trying to extinguish the scandal that you have so needlessly pitched us into.'

'What have you done?' Annabelle asked uneasily.

'I have spread to the four winds a very different story of your flight from England than the one your wretched brother told.'

'I hope it has more truth in it than his did!'

'In part it does. You ran away from Chilton, who was embezzling your inheritance while keeping you destitute, to seek the aid of your cousin, the Comte de Vergennes, in France. Now we come to the prevarication: you did not travel to Paris with me, nor were you living here with your cousin. I chanced to meet you at the Palais-Royal the day after the dinner at the British ambassador's, and you were quite amazed when I informed you that you were the scandal of London.'

'No one will believe that now,' she said bitterly. 'They will be certain that you brought me here, disguised as a governess, to be your convenient. Why should they think anything else?'

'Because I have never troubled to conceal my convenients from public view, their ranks have never included a lady of quality, and I have never made one of them my wife,' he said witheringly. 'Our marriage will confound the gossips.'

Since he looked and sounded as though he would much prefer to murder, rather than marry her, Annabelle could only stare at him in disbelief for a moment before saying with frigid hauteur, 'I am overcome by the honour you do me in seeking my hand, my most noble lord, but I must decline your kind offer.'

'It is not an offer—it is an order!' he snapped.

Her hauteur instantly deserted her. 'I won't marry you!'

'You do not have a choice,' he told her roughly. 'You forfeited it when you tricked me into bringing you to Paris. You little fool, you know as well as I that a high-born lady cannot travel through Europe under the protection of a man not her husband and not pay the piper. And what of my sister? What of the consequences of this contretemps on her?'

Annabelle's guilt about hurting Rachel overcame her anger, and she cried in agitation, 'I did not mean . . . I would not for the world have . . . I would do anything at all to rectify that.'

'I am happy to hear that, because the only possible way for you to do so is by marrying me, displeasing as it may be.'

'You cannot want to marry me merely to save your sister's reputation?' she cried, aghast.

He looked as though he wanted to strangle her. 'Can you think of any other reason why I should want to marry you?' he demanded savagely.

'None,' she assured him icily.

Her answer clearly infuriated him. 'What the deuce is the matter with you?' he demanded abruptly. 'You act as though I were the one who tricked *you*, not the other way around!'

'I had no intention of tricking you into marriage!' she cried. 'I told you the day we met that I had no designs on either your purse or your bachelorhood, and that was the truth.'

'What was your intention?'

'I told you, to escape my brother! How could you possibly think that I would plot anything with that evil little toad?' The dreadful pain and humiliation caused by Jason's ugly reading of her character suddenly overpowered her, and tears she was helpless to stop welled up in her eyes.

His expression softened, and he said quietly, 'Consider what a woman's deceit once cost me, Annabelle. Is it any wonder I was shocked and outraged beyond rational thought when I learned from your snake of a brother that you, too, had deceived me and that once again the price being demanded of me was marriage?'

In a small, broken voice which revealed the agony in her heart, she said, 'I don't blame you for being furious about my deceit. I deserve that. But surely, Jason, after all our weeks together, you knew me better than to think I could be in league with my dreadful brother.'

'Is that what you are so exercised about, vixen?' he asked roughly.

'Yes! And that is why I cannot marry you. You do not trust me.' Annabelle brushed ineffectually at her tears. 'Trust should be the foundation of marriage.'

'At last we agree on something! Yes, it should be. But what about your trust in me? You did not trust me enough to tell me who you were.'

'If I had done so, you would not have taken me to France with you.'

'Most likely I would not have. But surely, Annabelle, after all our weeks together,' he said, deliberately echoing her earlier words, 'you should have trusted me enough to confess the truth when I told you what Oldfield had said about you. Don't you think I deserved some warning of the scandal that was likely to break about my head?' He sighed wearily. 'How much easier it would have been for me to nip it then.'

Annabelle realised with a stricken conscience that Jason was justified in his anger on this point. She looked at him with eyes full of tears and silent contrition.

'Even after you accepted my offer to marry you, you still did not trust me enough to tell me the truth. You were guilty of a far more serious lack of trust than I was, and I won't scruple to tell you that I am still angry about it.'

A bright flush of shame stained her cheeks, already glistening with tears, and she admitted in a deeply mortified voice, 'Oh, Jason, I was such a fool!'

'Yes, you were,' he agreed. Removing a handkerchief from his pocket, he gently wiped away the tears from her cheeks. 'You don't know how close you came to being throttled earlier, you maddening baggage, when you tried to refuse to see me.'

'You looked so angry, I assumed you still thought me conspiring with my brother.'

'I would not be here if I thought that,' Jason said softly. He finished drying Annabelle's eyes and pocketed his handkerchief.

She said, her voice troubled, 'I cannot fathom why Frederick should have demanded that you marry me.'

'He wished to extract twenty thousand pounds from me in exchange for withdrawing the demand.'

Annabelle went white with anger and shame. 'How like that little toad! What did you tell him?'

Jason grinned. 'That the price was far too high and I preferred to marry you so that I might squander your great inheritance on my incognitas.'

She regarded him dubiously. 'You told me that even my large fortune could not tempt you to the altar with me.'

'It doesn't, my little vixen. Do you seriously think I would marry you for any reason other than that I love you and want to spend the rest of my life with you?' His voice was gentle, reproachful, with none of the harsh anger which had laced it earlier.

Her eyes widened. 'Not even to save your sister's reputation?'

'Ninnyhammer!' His smile was so full of love that Annabelle's heart was momentarily in danger of ceasing to beat. 'Fond as I have become of Rachel, I fear that sacrifice would still be beyond me.'

His mouth closed over Annabelle's in a long kiss that left no doubt in her mind as to the nature of his feelings for her.

Nevertheless, when he released her, she felt it imperative to give him one final chance to escape. 'You cannot want to marry me, Jason. I am not at all in your style.'

'My darling, you are precisely in my style. It was all those dazzling birds of paradise who were not.'

He apparently felt it necessary to reassure her on this point with a fierce embrace and another long kiss which left her so weak she was content to remain docilely, happily silent in his arms for a long moment.

'You know, my darling,' he said softly, 'I trusted you more than you give me credit for. You told me that no matter what else I believed, to believe that you loved me, and I did, or I would not have come here today.'

Annabelle's face glowed with happiness and sudden mischief. 'I fear I must confess I was not entirely truthful when I told you that I loved you,' she said, a provocative gleam in her eye.

Seeing it, his eyes narrowed warily. 'What is the truth, vixen?'

'I adore you!'

'I collect I will have to settle for that,' Jason said with mock resignation as he inclined his head to kiss her again.

2 NEW TITLES
FOR MARCH 1990

Jo *by Tracy Hughes.*
Book two in the sensational quartet of sisters in search of love…

In her latest cause, Jo's fiery nature helps her as an idealistic campaigner against the corrupting influence of the rock music industry. Until she meets the industry's heartbreaker, E. Z. Ellis, whose lyrics force her to think twice.   £2.99

Sally Bradford's debut novel **The Arrangement** is a poignant romance that will appeal to readers everywhere.

Lawyer, Juliet Cavanagh, wanted a child, but not the complications of a marriage. Brady Talcott answered her advertisement for a prospective father, but he had conditions of his own…   £2.99

W❍RLDWIDE

Available from Boots, Martins, John Menzies, W.H. Smith, Woolworths and other paperback stockists.

SOLITAIRE – Lisa Gregory   £3.50

Emptiness and heartache lay behind the facade of Jennifer Taylor's
glittering Hollywood career. Bitter betrayal had driven her to
become a successful actress, but now at the top, where else
could she go?

SWEET SUMMER HEAT – Katherine Burton   £2.99

Rebecca Whitney has a great future ahead of her until a sultry
encounter with a former lover leaves her devastated...

THE LIGHT FANTASTIC – Peggy Nicholson   £2.99

In this debut novel, Peggy Nicholson focuses on her own
profession... Award-winning author Tripp Wetherby's fear of
flying could ruin the promotional tour for his latest blockbuster.
Rennie Markell is employed to cure his phobia, whatever it takes!

These three new titles will be out in bookshops from February 1990.

W🌐RLDWIDE

Mills & Boon

HELP US TO GET TO KNOW YOU

and help yourself to "Passionate Enemy" by Patricia Wilson

Patricia Wilson's classic Romance isn't available in the shops but can be yours FREE when you complete and post the simple questionnaire overleaf

Mills & Boon

ROMANCE

Passionate Enemy

PATRICIA WILSON

FREE

Romance Survey

If you could spare a minute to answer a few simple questions about your romantic fiction reading, we'll send you in return a FREE copy of "Passionate Enemy" by Patricia Wilson.

The information you provide will help us to get to know you better, and give you more of what you want from your romance reading.

Don't forget to fill in your name and address – so we know where to send your FREE book!

SEE OVER

Just answer these simple questions for your FREE book

1 Who is your
favourite author? _____

2 The last romance you read
(apart from this one) was? _____

3 How many Mills & Boon Romances
have you bought in the last 6 months? _____

4 How did you first hear about Mills & Boon? *(Tick one)*
❑ Friend   ❑ Television   ❑ Magazines or newspapers
❑ Saw them in the shops   ❑ Received a mailing
❑ other *(please describe)* _____

5 Where did you get this book?
_____

6 Which age
group are you in?
❑ Under 24   ❑ 25-34   ❑ 35-44
❑ 45-54   ❑ 55-64   ❑ Over 65

7 After you read your
Mills & Boon novels,
what do you do with them?
❑ Keep them ❑ Give them away
❑ Lend them to friends
❑ Other*(Please describe)*
_____
_____

8 What do you like about Mills & Boon Romances?
_____

9 Are you a Mills & Boon subscriber?   ❑ Yes   ❑ No

---

*Fill in your name and address, put this page in an envelope
and post TODAY to:* Mills & Boon Reader Survey,
FREEPOST, P.O. Box 236, Croydon, Surrey. CR9 9EL

**NO
STAMP
NEEDED**

Name (Mrs. / Miss. / Ms. / Mr.) _____

Address _____

_____ Postcode _____

You may be mailed with offers
as a result of this questionnaire

PWQ1